STEVE
FLETCHER

U. S. MARINE

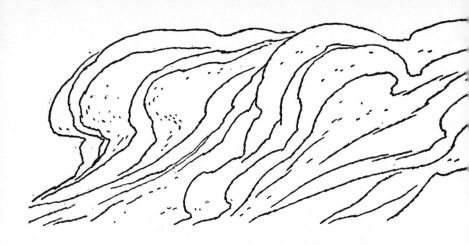

A STORY OF RECRUIT
TRAINING IN THE MARINE CORPS

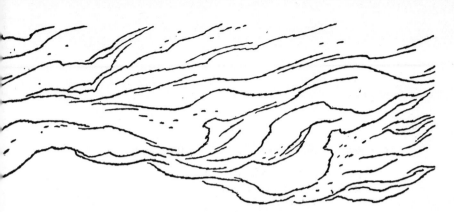

STEVE FLETCHER

U. S. MARINE

BY CHARLES F. JOHNSON

Illustrations by Oliver Grimley

HOLT, RINEHART AND WINSTON
New York

PUBLISHED, SEPTEMBER, 1957
SECOND PRINTING, JANUARY, 1962

Library of Congress Catalog Card Number: 57-10195

94675–0212

Printed in the United States of America

ABOUT THE AUTHOR

CHARLES FREDERICK JOHNSON has been writing, for various sources and in various veins, since his years in college. At Trinity College, he was managing editor of the weekly newspaper. After graduation he served in the Marine Corps, and when the war ended, Johnson went to Connecticut and worked for several newspapers, later joining the editorial staff of a publishing company in Chicago.

In 1951, Johnson was recalled by the Marines; he left a job as article writer for the company magazine at the Dartnell Publishing Company. His Marine duty took him to Camp Lejeune and then to San Diego. At both commands he was public information officer and editor of the company newspaper. Before returning to civilian life, he served on a special assignment for three months at Headquarters, U. S. Marine Corps, writing a manual for public information and camp newspaper personnel.

Johnson returned from service and became aviation and military writer for *The San Diego Union*. He soon became an editorial writer, a duty he still has.

Johnson's service career was many-sided. He served as an aerologist and an MP after completing his recruit training at Parris Island and before being assigned to officer candidate school, Quantico, Virginia. He was trained as a rifle platoon leader and commissioned a second lieutenant in 1945. These varied experiences served as a basis for writing a keen, first-hand account of Marine training, discipline and esprit de corps.

The author says that he started this book of fiction about the Marine Corps because he was ". . . convinced that it (the service) was an experience from which any normal U. S. youth could profit."

Contents

Chapter 1

TOO CLOSE TO THE TREE

THE rangy boy pushed the long strands of blond hair out of his eyes. Stretching out once again over the fender of his hot rod, he reached under the hood. His fingers, slippery with grease, grasped a metal coupling which channeled air from the supercharger to the carburetor's thick throat. For 15 minutes he'd been trying to push the coupling over the 'charger's port and hold it there while he tightened a clamp.

"There," he whispered suddenly, "got it!" He reached for an electric screwdriver and quickly ran the bolt down tight.

Straightening his 6-foot frame, Steve Fletcher picked up the tools which had accumulated on the fender and motor of his racer, slammed the hood down and walked over to a workbench where he dropped the tools. As he wiped his hands on a piece of waste cloth, he strolled over to a door and opened it.

"Roger," he called across the lawn to his house, "yo, Roger."

A younger boy's face popped out of an upstair's window. "Whataya want, Steve?"

"Got the new supercharger hooked up. If you wanna be here when I give 'er a try, better move it."

"Be right down," the lad answered, his happy face disappearing as quickly as it had appeared. A few moments later the kitchen door opened and slammed shut; Roger Fletcher trotted down the brick path and into the 2-car garage.

He stared admiringly at his brother's roadster. "The 'Red Rocket' sure looks sharp, Stevie. When do you think Dad will let you take her out for a short spin?"

The older boy's face darkened and he rubbed the heel of his hand slowly across his chin and along his jaw. "Beats me," he responded ruefully. "But chances sure didn't look bright this afternoon."

"How's that?"

"Why the last thing Dad did as he and Mom drove out of here for the beach was stick his head out of the car window and warn me not to get any ideas about takin' the hot rod out."

Both boys turned to admire the "Red Rocket." Though it had originally been a sedate, square-shaped 1931 Ford coupé, it now looked as sleek as a European road racer.

Steve had run across the old relic, wheelless and resting on its axles, in the rear of a used-car lot. He quickly bought it with three 5-dollar bills he'd been saving for just such a chance. After getting wheels for it, his father towed the old wreck home.

There in the garage Steve cut off the Ford's top with an acetylene torch. Its mudguards, running boards and bumpers he sheared off in the same way. The ripped and faded mohair upholstery he replaced with pleated red leather.

Steve not only covered the seats and insides of the doors with this but also brought the leather up and over the edges of the doors and the back of the seat. With this padded, leather edging, the midsection of the Ford resembled the cockpit of an old-fashioned, open airplane.

A slimmer, smaller radiator superseded the original square and bulky one. To accomplish this, the hood had to be tailored down to fit. Steve sloped it down and also cut a row of parallel slices in the top; then he bent up the edges of these incisions, giving the hood the look of louvered house shutters. This not only looked good but helped cool the motor.

By using much bigger tires on the rear wheels and installing "dropped" axles, Steve had given his speedster a low, rakish, sloping profile.

The body he rubbed right down to bright metal and then sprayed with a brilliant red lacquer. He applied 24 coats, using up 3½ gallons of the expensive paint. He tipped the ends of the dual exhausts with long, chrome-plated throats. These and the hot rod's huge Rolls Royce headlights, which Steve had found in a junkyard, were the only chrome parts. All the rest was a gleaming red.

"Now to fire 'er off and see how that new supercharger feeds compressed air to the carburetor," Steve announced, vaulting into the seat. "How about opening the garage doors, Rog? Both of them."

As his brother speedily set about this task, Steve adjusted the choke and spark.

"All clear," Roger Fletcher yelled from the apron of the garage.

Without turning, Steve bent over the steering wheel and stepped on the starter button. He listened with an expression of deep concentration, almost a frown, as the motor sluggishly groaned over. It started once, then again, but quickly stalled both times. At last it roared into a steady series of explosions which seemed to shake the garage.

"That's real power, Steve," shouted Roger above the racket, his fists clenched over his head in the victory sign.

Steve tinkered with the choke and spark and managed to smooth out the motor's performance and slow it down. Roger watched him intently, his eyes sparkling with delighted excitement.

"Hop in," the older boy invited, pointing to the seat beside him.

When his brother was snugly settled in the seat, Steve began to ease the hot rod out of the garage. "Not so hard on the ears out here in the open," he explained. "Besides, I don't think that Dad would object to *this*."

After driving the car up and down the long, graveled driveway for a while, testing the motor, Steve cut the switch and coasted to a halt in front of the garage.

"Mixture's too rich. Think I'll thin it down a trifle." With that, he hopped out of the Ford and went into the garage.

By the time he had reappeared, bearing a screwdriver and a set of socket wrenches, Roger had lifted the hood, exposing the chrome-plated motor, its starter, generator and water pump painted a bright yellow.

Steve thanked his brother and set to work unloosening a circle of nuts on the carburetor.

Roger peered under the hood, fascinated by his brother's deft fingers. Roger was 13 years old, five years his brother's junior and proportionately smaller. Steve was long and lean; Roger was short and round. But he was not fat, though a barreled chest made him appear rotund. His brown hair was clipped short in a "butch." His eyes were merry and sparkling. When he saw that his brother had finished adjusting the carburetor so that it admitted a little more air and a little less gasoline, Roger broke the silence. "D'ya think Dad'll *ever* let you take the 'Rocket' for a spin?"

Steve looked up from his work. "Someday, sure. He's sore at me now because I spent so much time last fall working on this 'bomb.' Then I didn't make my letter in football because I got benched for smoking. That didn't help. Neither did the class I flunked at midterm."

"But you graduated in June, Steve," his brother protested. "And won your third track letter."

"Yes, but I didn't get accepted by any decent college, especially Amherst. That's what really hurt him. You'll understand that better when he starts beatin' the drums for you to go to Amherst, dear old 'Lord Jeff' where he went, where grandpa went and all the Fletchers have *always* gone."

"Well, I hope you can get into some college soon, Steve. Maybe Dad'll let you take the 'Rocket' out for a spin then."

By this time Steve had tightened down the adjusting nuts.

He slammed the hood closed and fastened it. Thinking about his father's, and less consciously about his own responsibility for it, resentment and frustration flared within him. He looked at his brother, blurted out, "Why wait any longer?" and clambered into the hot rod.

Startled by the angry burst and sudden action, Roger watched his brother in amazement. "Steve, Steve," he finally shouted, "you're not going to disobey Dad, are you?"

"You don't have to look at it that way," Steve replied more calmly than before. "He'll never know. And what he doesn't know won't hurt him—or me."

Roger continued to stare at his brother, who already was behind the wheel and preparing to start his racer.

"Dad'll never know, Rog," he argued. "We'll be back in 15, 20 minutes. They won't be home for an hour yet."

The younger brother made not a move.

"Say," Steve spoke, his voice growing louder, "you're comin' along. You're not goin' to play chicken on me, are you?"

"You go; I'll go." Roger snapped, walking resolutely around to his side of the car. "But wouldn't it be better if we both obeyed Dad's order?"

"Dad's order. Dad's order," the older brother repeated impatiently. "That's all I hear around here. Sure, he was a hero in the Marines during World War II. I'm proud of it. But I wish he'd forget some of that Marine Corps discipline. I've been working 8 months on this mill and now I'm going to find out what she can do; when Dad finally does get around to letting me take it out officially, I'll tell him about this. I'll bet he really gets a big laugh out of the way we tricked him."

He flipped on the ignition and stepped on the starter. The hot rod started with a roar. Before they reached the end of the driveway, Steve had shifted into second gear; he slowed down slightly as the car swung into the wide street in front of the Fletcher home. The car was in high gear by the time it straightened out from a tight, tire-screeching turn.

Steve's slight feelings of guilt and fear of being caught by his father were soon drowned by thrill and pride as they zipped through the streets, the racer's red body glistening in the afternoon sunlight.

"Hey, Steve, what ya got in your hand?" Roger pointed to a round dial about the size of a pocket watch which his brother cupped in his left hand.

"It's a 'tack'—tachometer. The needle on the dial points to crankshaft speed in r.p.m.'s. We're turning up 2,800 right now. You compare tack readin's with the speedometer. Hot-rodders try to get up as much speed as possible while keepin' the tack readin' low. Shows you're a good driver."

They were now out of the city, speeding along a fairly narrow macadam road surrounded on both sides by orange groves. The highway itself was lined with tall eucalyptus trees whose slender, sparsely leafed branches stirred gently in the afternoon breeze that was beginning to stir from the Pacific Ocean, 10 miles to the west.

The Fletchers lived in California, in a middle-sized town about 40 miles north of San Francisco. They had lived there since the end of the war in 1945 when Mr. Fletcher came out of the Marine Corps to resume his law career, interrupted when he enlisted in 1940.

Being behind the wheel of his own car—guiding it around curves, listening to the throaty, authoritative roar from its twin exhaust pipes—excited Steve more and more. Almost by instinct, he began to steer toward a section on the outskirts of town that was very familiar to him—"the Strip."

Nearing a quiet, deserted stretch of highway, he saw the gang up ahead, a strange mixture of bobby soxers, boys in tight levis and dark gaucho shirts. Their brightly colored hot rods were strung in a disorderly line along the edge of the road. As Steve drove up to the crowd, he noticed some strange faces and cars, outsiders from a nearby town.

The "Red Rocket" created a stir of admiration and some squeals of excitement from the teen-age group.

"So ya busted out with her, huh, Steve?"

"Not bad for an old Ford!"

"When can I have a ride—or are you going to keep that gorgeous thing for men only?"

One of the newcomers, a short boy whose black hair was combed in elaborate swirls, didn't contribute to Steve's welcome. Instead he walked appraisingly around the "Rocket," kicking the tires and slapping the hood contemptuously. Then he looked up at Steve's puzzled face.

"Not bad, not bad. Can it move?"

"It moves, Buddy. Don't worry, it moves," Steve assured him.

"How about the driver?" the short lad asked pugnaciously. "Does he move? Does he want a tag match on the Strip, maybe?"

Steve was on the spot and he knew it. He had given up tag racing when he'd had an accident 2 years ago. But now he was being challenged in front of his friends and knew that he couldn't back down. Yet his father had forbidden him even to take his hot rod out of the garage.

"Not chicken, are ya?" his antagonist sneered.

Steve responded by starting his engine and gunning it to a loud crescendo. Turning to his rival, he shouted, "Get into your heap and let's go!"

Like a pair of jet fighters roaring down a carrier's flight-deck, the two sleek hot rods gathered speed along the nearly deserted stretch of highway. Bent low and frozen into position behind the wheel, Steve Fletcher shouted to his brother, "Down, down! Keep your head below the slip stream so you don't slow us."

Less than 8 feet away, behind the wheel of a silvery, tapered V-8, the dark, curlyheaded youth hunched and occasionally glanced over at Steve with a faint smirk. The two cars were almost one as their wheels whirled, separated by less than a foot and that distance steadily narrowing as they streaked over the hot concrete road.

The two hot-rodders raced along, trying to see how fast they could go and at what speed they could touch hubcaps without spinning off the course.

Roger kept his eyes tightly closed except for furtive looks at the speedometer. The needle had swept around to 90 miles an hour, then seemed to bounce around crazily and advance no further. Roger knew that the victor's laurels in a game of hot-rod tag went to the driver who was going faster when contact was broken off. He wondered if the "Red Rocket" had the speed to win.

Though the swiftly rushing wind made his eyes bleary, Roger raised his head and looked over at the rival racer. He was falling behind! Slowly, almost imperceptively at first, then with a sudden rush, the V-8 decreased speed.

Steve, seemingly hypnotized by the will to win, failed to notice that the "Red Rocket" now had the road to itself.

Roger glanced up the highway. He realized in a flash why the hot-rodder had abruptly defaulted: the Strip came to a sudden end in a sharp curve only a few hundred yards away. He looked over at his brother who was still frozen at the wheel, his eyes riveted on the highway immediately ahead.

"Steve, Steve!" he shouted. "We're coming to the end of the straightaway!"

This warning cry broke the older boy's spell. He quickly lifted his eyes and saw to his horror that there was not an instant to lose. He shifted his foot from accelerator to brake pedal.

But when he began to apply pressure, his heart felt as though it had stopped. The brakes seemed to have no effect on the speeding vehicle! Then the motor, slowing down for lack of gas, began to act as a brake itself. The speedometer indicator retreated . . . 85, 80, 70, 65.

Will we make it? thought Steve. He judged the distance.

About one-eighth of a mile remained before the road took a sharp turn to the left—less than 250 yards.

Roger could read alarm on his brother's face. He tightened his grip and braced himself, feet planted on the floorboards and shoulders forced against the back of the seat. Roadside trees blurred by.

"Hold tight, Rog; don't think we can make it," Steve bellowed over the scream of the wind and the car noise.

The hot rod roared into the curve. It was particularly sharp just before it straightened out—and it had never been banked. As if some huge and hungry giant were trying to grasp it to his chest, the light racer was pulled wider and wider by centrifugal force. First the right front wheel, then the right rear dropped from the concrete onto the bumpy shoulder.

Steve had an iron two-handed grip on the steering wheel. As the car's speed lessened, the brakes became more effective. Steve did not push down on them too hard, knowing that any sudden force would overturn the car or, just as bad, force it into a spin, lashing it against a tree.

A row of eucalyptus trees which bordered the turn every 15 or 20 feet got closer and closer. The car was now completely off the surfaced portion of the highway and shocks from the knobby, uneven shoulders were almost wrenching the steering wheel from Steve's hands.

By wonderfully skilled driving, Steve fought the hot rod almost all the way around the curve. Though a great cloud of dust enveloped the car and cut down visibility, his hopes rose.

But there was another menace, one which the swirling dust obscured—a tree slightly closer to the road than the rest. Suddenly, it loomed up. Steve saw it out of the corner of his right eye. He swerved as abruptly as he dared. He thought that they would scrape by.

It was close. All they needed was 2 inches. It was 2 inches they didn't have.

The racer's right front wheel thudded against the thick trunk of the tree. Next the radiator and frame hit. In a thousandth of a second the impact had halted the speeding hot rod.

Not so the occupants. The force of inertia threw Steve against the steering wheel. This pushed into his stomach and against his ribs. As if a black hood had been dropped over his head, unconsciousness engulfed him.

He knew no more.

Chapter 2

DISOBEDIENCE COLLECTS ITS TOLL

THE rapid pounding in his head slowed down and the darkness before his eyes lightened. For a moment Steve thought that he was in some deep tunnel, similar to a mine shaft, gradually approaching daylight. The pulsating noise sounded like reports from a powerful engine, bouncing around in the vaulted chamber.

Steve groped about, trying to orient himself. Shifting his position, he realized that he was flat on his back. He reached out and touched something. It seemed familiar, but his benumbed mind couldn't recognize it. He rubbed the tips of his fingers over it, straining to identify it. It felt fuzzy. Suddenly Steve knew that it was a blanket. He was lying in bed!

But where? He still could see but dimly. Struggle as he would, he couldn't lift his hands to pull away whatever covered his face. When he raised his arms, the pain in his chest was so excruciating he couldn't breathe.

What happened? he asked himself. Where am I?

The pain continued, but his mind was clearing. Soon pieces of the afternoon's experience began to emerge in his memory. He recalled driving out to the Strip with Roger. Then his mind flashed back to the earlier episode in front of the garage.

He could see Roger's face, wreathed with smiles and his eyes sparkling. This mental image bothered Steve; there was something disquieting about it. He questioned himself, trying to remember some fact to explain this puzzling emotion.

Then he recalled the gang of hot-rodders who had gathered at the Strip, the surly challenge from the swarthy driver, the tag match with him and the losing battle to fight the "Red Rocket" around the sharp curve which ended the straightaway.

There had been an accident!

This realization hit Steve Fletcher like a sledge. He had disobeyed his father, taken the hot rod out for a trial run, and cracked it up. Then a new question arose to terrify him. Had Roger survived the accident, or had he been killed?

Steve realized that Roger, with no steering wheel to cling to, had probably been thrown from the topless roadster. If he had hit one of the trees or had landed in the irrigation ditch, Roger was dead. And I killed him, he thought with horror.

Then for the first time since he regained consciousness, Steve heard voices, low and indistinct, but voices. He listened hard, trying to catch what was being said.

"The X-rays show only four cracked ribs, Mrs. Fletcher. No major bones in the back or chest were broken. We worried about the pancreas. That usually is damaged in accidents where the driver is thrown against the steering wheel, but Steve's a heavily muscled boy. He rammed the wheel violently but didn't rupture anything."

"How long will he have to stay here, Dr. Bishart?" Steve recognized his mother's voice. He tried to speak to her, to call out to her and ask about Roger. But he had no control over his tongue or lips. He couldn't make a sound.

The doctor went on, "Barring complications, you should have him home in a week or 10 days. But I'm not promising that. We'll know better when we take the sutures out of his forehead and scalp."

Steve realized why his head throbbed so with pain and why he couldn't see. I laid open my head, he thought, and they've stitched it up and bandaged me below my eyes.

"Nurse tells me that Steve is stirring." It was the doctor's voice again. "We're going to give him another sedative so he'll sleep through the rest of the night. And, say, you'd better get some rest yourself. Roger will be in surgery for several more hours. Why not stretch out and take a nap like Mr. Fletcher is doing?"

Roger is alive! The happy discovery surged through Steve's mind and heart. The doctor's words lifted a heavy load of fear and suspense from his mind. But his brother was still in danger. Steve wanted to find out more. He felt the sheets and blankets being lifted, then a sharp needle jabbed him. In a few moments he drifted off to sleep.

When Steve awoke next, he was fully conscious. The bandage that swathed his head stopped at the bridge of his nose. By tilting his head back, he could peer out and see sections of his hospital room. He turned to one side and was surprised to see a pretty, young nurse sitting in a chair beside his bed. She looked up at him and smiled.

"Good morning, Swami Fletcher," she said brightly. "Let's cut that turban of yours off. We had to put on a big bandage the first night to protect the hemstitching the doctor did on your head."

She snipped the bulky gauze off with a pair of shears. As she started to put on a smaller dressing, Steve worked up courage to ask the dreaded question. "Is my brother . . . is Roger okay?"

The nurse's face darkened and her manner changed. "I'm not supposed to tell. . . ."

Steve bit down on his teeth and held his breath.

The nurse spoke again, "Your brother's having a rough time. He was in surgery for 5 or 6 hours last night, but he's holding his own now."

"Can you tell me how bad he's hurt?" Steve asked fearfully.

"I've talked too much already," the nurse replied, pulling his lips together with her fingers. "Besides, you need some food. Your mother and dad will be back to see you in a few minutes. They're downstairs in the drugstore having some toast and coffee."

She disappeared, returning soon with a tray of orange juice, eggs and bacon, toast and coffee. Steve picked at his breakfast, but his mind was on other things. He tried to figure out why he had been such a fool. He pictured his brother, his body broken and bearing for life the scars which he, supposedly the younger boy's protector, had caused him to suffer. He tried to imagine how he could live if Roger died.

What would his parents think of him? Steve ticked off in his mind the number of times in the last year that he had disobeyed, disappointed and humiliated them—getting cut from the football squad when he was co-captain, receiving those poor marks during his senior year, failing to get admitted to Amherst where his father and grandfather had gone, and generally showing his parents contempt and disrespect.

I guess I haven't got what it takes to make a real man, Steve reproached himself.

As he reached this humiliating conclusion, the door opened and his mother tiptoed into the room, followed by his father. Mrs. Fletcher, seeing her son sitting up in bed, exclaimed excitedly, "Steve, Steve, you're awake!" She rushed over and, leaning carefully over the bed, kissed him tenderly on the cheek.

His father followed her over, but much more slowly. "Steve, son," the words came soberly, "it's good to see you sitting up. You don't look half-bad."

"Thanks, Dad," Steve responded, looking up at his father's face and seeing a deep coldness there.

"Mom and Dad, please tell me! How's Roger? He'll live won't he?" For the first time since he was a little boy, Steve Fletcher whimpered and tears rolled down his cheeks.

It was his mother who spoke. "The doctors feel pretty sure now that Rog will pull through. He's still unconscious and in an oxygen tent. But he's gaining strength. We almost lost him last night."

"What happened to him?" Steve's voice was frantic, and he looked beseechingly first at his mother, then at his father.

It was Mr. Fletcher who answered. "They found you unconscious in the car; the wheel stopped you. For a while the highway patrolmen and the wrecker's crew didn't even know that there was a second person in the car with you.

"Roger was thrown clear of your hot rod. He missed the tree, apparently by inches, they tell me, and landed on the other side of the irrigation ditch in the orange grove.

"Because the accident happened in the late afternoon it was dusk by the time the ambulance and wrecker arrived. One of the policemen just managed to see Roger's figure there, crumpled in the earth underneath a tree."

"Is Rog hurt bad?" Steve asked, his voice barely audible.

There was silence for a moment, then Mr. Fletcher replied, "Nothing much worse than a broken neck."

His father's sarcasm cut Steve as though he'd been lashed across the face. He realized then that whether Roger lived or died, it would be hard, probably impossible for him to win back his father's love and respect.

Chapter 3

A FATHER'S ULTIMATUM

STEVE'S stay in the hospital lasted little longer than a week, as the doctor predicted. When he first arrived home, his mother was overly attentive and kept a special eye on him. His father, however, still maintained a cold reserve which let Steve know that he still wasn't forgiven for his escapade. He'd been out of the hospital for 8 weeks when his father announced one night at the dinner table that Steve's case was coming up in juvenile court the next morning.

"Juvenile court?" blurted out Steve.

"That's right, Steve, juvenile court," his father responded curtly. "You didn't think you could drive around the state's highways, crack up cars, and smash up a few people without the police noticing it, did you?"

Steve made no reply. He kept wondering what they could do to him. His father was a lawyer, but would he stick by him now? The boy could only sit and wonder. Soon he pushed away from the table, excused himself, and went up to his room for the rest of the evening.

The next morning Steve and Mr. Fletcher made their appearance at the city hall with its austere marble halls and frosted doors of glass with different names on each. Mr. Fletcher motioned him through a door on which "Santa Rosa County Juvenile Court, Judge Clifford R. Schaible" was printed. Steve felt a little relieved when he remembered that his dad knew Judge Schaible.

His case was the first on the docket that morning, so he

and his father sat quietly in the small courtroom where the private juvenile hearings were held. Soon a portly bailiff announced that the Court would come to order. Everyone arose as the judge, a tall, lean man dressed in a black robe, entered the courtroom and sat in front of a long table at its head.

Steve listened penitently, his chin sunk on his chest, as the nervous prosecutor read the charge, relating the various laws which Steve and his fellow hot-rodders had broken. The judge sat quietly, shuffling through the sheets of paper in front of him.

When the prosecutor was finished, the grim-faced judge spoke in a loud voice that indicated he was not in a friendly mood, "All right, Steve, what do you have to say for yourself? Just what's wrong with you anyway, Boy? I never expected to see you here, but you've been leading up to this—getting kicked off the football team, making poor grades. Oh, we've got your whole record here. And it isn't too good. Seems as if you're trying to work your way into the boy's reformatory. Is that right?"

"No, Judge Schaible," Steve replied without taking his eyes off the floor.

"Look at me when you talk, Steve," the judge continued. "What's wrong with you? You come from a good home, I know your father, and he does all he can for you. You're not living in the slums. Can't you find some other friends beside that hot-rod crowd?"

Steve felt it futile to reply, for the judge was not really asking him questions. He was "roasting" Steve, and Steve knew it. Finally, when he was feeling thoroughly miserable, the judge raised his voice even louder and said, "Well, Steve, now what do you think we ought to do with you to keep you out of trouble?"

Steve looked up weakly, shook his head. Before he could speak, the probation officer, who had been sitting off to the right of the judge, broke into the dialogue.

"Your Honor, I think his father has a good suggestion that

the Court should consider," volunteered the probation officer.

From immediately behind him his father rose and spoke to the judge, "Your Honor, I hope you won't find it necessary to send Steve away or put him on probation. I think he can be straightened out, but he needs more help than either his mother or I can give him. For that reason, I'm requesting that he be permitted to enlist in the Marines. He'll be eighteen in another week and if the Marines will take him, I think they can make a man out of him."

Steve was stunned at the idea that he should join the Marine Corps. The more he thought about it, the less the prospect appealed to him. Me a marine! he shuddered. What a farce!

The suspicion raced through his mind that the whole plan had been engineered by his father out of court—the probation officer and the judge and the prosecuting attorney were all his friends.

"How do you feel about this, Stephen?" the judge inquired, breaking into his chain of thoughts.

For a moment he could say nothing. He knew what he *wanted* to say but could not summon the necessary moral courage. Realizing that his indecision was becoming embarrassingly prolonged he blurted out, "I think it's a pretty good idea. I'll do my best, anyway."

"Fine," Judge Schaible beamed. "Your case will be suspended pending final report of the probation officer."

Steve did not understand how all this was to be carried out. He hoped to be able to talk it over with his father but since his dad's law practice involved him in another case in Superior Court there was no time for a full explanation. In the meanwhile Steve felt that there must be some way to modify the sentence. Maybe military school.

The subject did not come up that night at home. Most of the talk involved Roger's release from the hospital the following day.

After a 9-week siege, Roger did come home the next

afternoon. His once round face was thin, pallid and a heavy cast—chin high—immobilized his neck, chest and shoulders.

At dinner that night the Fletchers celebrated. His mother cooked Roger's favorite meal of thick porterhouse steak, french fried onions and mashed potatoes which served as a basin for a pond of thick gravy. Propped up by pillows, the guest of honor was able to sit at the table. But, tired by the exertion and excitement, he had to go back to bed before dessert was served.

So the rest of the Fletchers went up with Roger to his bedroom and ate cake and ice cream, sitting on and around his bed. By the time they had finished, Roger's eyelids began to droop and he started to drowse. The others tiptoed out of the room.

Steve started to help his mother take the dessert dishes downstairs, but his father touched his arm and motioned him into a small, book-lined den just next to Roger's room.

Shutting the door quietly, his father announced in a firm voice, "Steve, I think the time's come for you and me to talk things over. A lot of things. Sit down."

The boy dropped into the heavy leather chair his father pointed to, but was oblivious to its comforts. The doomsday he'd long been dreading had arrived.

The elder Fletcher seated himself in a swivel chair at a desk and spun himself around to confront his son. He said nothing for a few moments. Then, after what seemed to be a long time to Steve, he began.

"As you've probably noticed, Steve, I haven't mentioned the accident from that first day in the hospital until right now. But Roger's home now, on the mend, and apparently not going to suffer any permanent injuries. It's a miracle you both weren't killed. So what needs to be said to you needs to be said badly—and now."

Steve looked down at the floor and nodded his head. "I got it coming, Dad," he admitted.

"You sure have!" His father's tone was quick, emphatic.

"For the past year or so you've been in one scrape after another; you've been a continual trial to your mother and me; you've disobeyed us time after time; you just squeaked through your senior year of school; you were such a horrible example that the coach kicked you off the football team; you've dressed and acted like a fool. And then the accident. When you took that ridiculous car out of the garage you deliberately disobeyed me, didn't you?"

"Yes, I guess so, Dad," Steve replied meekly.

"But you did more than that. You broke your own word of honor. That's what worries your mother and me most. You not only seem to have lost all respect for us, but respect for yourself, too."

"Dad, I think I can straighten myself out. . . . When I get away to college, I'll settle down, honest I will."

His father snorted in disgust. "That's a laugh, Steve. Even if I believed that you would—which I don't—we couldn't send you to college."

"Why not?" the boy queried.

"That accident of yours took every penny your mother and I saved. We may even have to mortgage the house again before we're through paying all the bills from your accident."

This revelation shocked Steve. He hadn't given any thought to all the expenses for doctors and hospital care needed by himself—and Roger even more so. Looking up at his father he asked, "Well, what's going to happen to me?"

"You're going to enlist in the Marine Corps—just as Judge Schaible decided yesterday." His father's voice was firm.

Partly because of the excitement engendered by Roger's return home and partly because the Marine prospect was so unpleasant that he had buried it in the back of his mind, Steve hadn't thought much that day about his becoming a marine.

Startled by the brusque reminder, Steve spoke out, "Me a marine?" in a tone part question, part contempt.

"Yes, you a marine," was his father's emphatic answer.

Steve rose to his feet and protested, "But I don't want to join."

"Sit down in that chair before I push you down," Mr. Fletcher demanded.

Steve fell back into his seat.

His father came closer and, looking down into Steve's face, declared, "When I was in the Marines during World War II I saw the corps' training and tradition make men out of many a bum—give them self-respect and a sense of responsibility; teach them what integrity, duty, reliability meant."

"Dad," Steve interrupted, "I'm proud that you were a Marine officer. But I've heard all this before. Please tell me where I fit in."

"Steve, I hate to say this to any son of mine, but you asked for it. You're on your way to becoming a completely worth-less individual. I have come to the conclusion that only a hitch in the Marine Corps can save you."

"What if war breaks out!" Steve exclaimed.

"Your chances in the Marine Corps are as good as anyplace else. Maybe better, because you'll be better trained, better led. Don't let your age worry you. I even had some 16-year-old kids in my rifle company on Guadalcanal in 1942. Lied about their age and the recruiting officers were too busy to check."

Realizing that his father was determined, Steve decided to try a new tack. "I don't care what happens. I won't enlist in the Marine Corps."

Mr. Fletcher's eyes flashed with anger. "Then I'll put it to you straight: Either you become a marine or I'll have you sent away to reform school."

"What?" Steve cried, frowning and incredulous.

"You've been arrested for speeding, driving so as to endan-ger and several other nice, juicy charges. Maybe you didn't understand it yesterday but Judge Schaible released you in my custody. I can turn you back any time I want to. Then they'd lock you up in jail. When you came up for final trial—yesterday was only a pretrial hearing—you'd get about a year on each charge. After 3 years in reform school, you'd come out a real bum."

Steve now realized that his father had him completely cornered. After a few moments of silence he said slowly, "Okay, I'll join the Marine Corps."

"You'll try to join the Marine Corps," his father interjected. "The standards are high and they've got tough mental and physical exams you'll have to get by. The recruiting officer may not like that police record of yours."

"What police record?" Steve asked scornfully.

"The local police blotter has a brief but interesting account of your attempt to break the sound barrier and of the criminal charges against you, resulting therefrom."

"Oh," moaned Steve.

"You better be getting to bed. I'm taking you down to the recruiting office at 8:00 a.m. tomorrow. For you that's early."

His father got up and left the room.

Steve sat there alone for a few moments. When he heard his father's footsteps downstairs, he rose and went into his bedroom. Undressing quickly, he got in bed. Looking up at the ceiling in his darkened room, many thoughts raced through his mind. One, however, kept returning—what adventures, sad or good, awaited him as Pvt. Steve Fletcher, United States Marine?

Chapter 4

TAKING THE PLUNGE

A FEW minutes before 8 o'clock the next morning, the Fletchers, father and son, walked into the Marine Corps recruiting station on the second floor of the local post office. A marine, in dress jacket and blue trousers with brilliant, scarlet N.C.O. stripes, was busy at a desk.

As the pair walked into the room, the marine, with the chevrons of a master sergeant—three upward-pointing stripes and three "rockers" below—looked up. A friendly smile spread across his face and he stood up. "Why good morning, Colonel Fletcher," he exclaimed. "Nice to have you aboard."

Seeing that Steve's father was surprised at being recognized, the sergeant quickly explained, "Sir, I met you at the Marine Corps Birthday Ball last November at the Memorial Club in San Francisco."

"Oh, sure, I remember," Mr. Fletcher exclaimed.

"My name's Bowen, Colonel," the master sergeant continued. "What can I do to help you?" Before there was a chance for a reply, he broke in, "But let me draw you some 'joe.' How d'ya like it?"

"Black for me. My son here takes it with cream and sugar. Right, Steve?"

"That's right, Dad," the boy responded in a quiet voice. He felt strangely shy and ill at ease.

The sergeant went into a small anteroom for the coffee, giving Steve a chance to look around. The room, except for

23

the walls, was barren. The walls were covered with large
colored posters depicting World War II fighting in the Pacific
—marines attacking through the ruins of an oriental temple
on Saipan, the shattered palms of Betio Island, Tarawa Atoll,
the ashen shores of Iwo Jima, the wet jungle of Guadalcanal.

There was a section devoted to Korea. On a map of that
peninsula was drawn the position of the 1st Marine Division,
just north of Seoul, guarding the traditional invasion route
to that much-beleaguered city. Steve was just walking over
to take a closer look at some of the 8″ x 10″ photographs of
Korean battle scenes tacked to the wall, when Bowen returned with the coffee.

"Here," he laughed merrily, "this'll get the old ticker really
started for the day."

Steve's father seated himself and, cradling the heavy crock-
ery cup in both hands, began, "Bowen, I wouldn't have come
in here this morning if I thought I'd be recognized. I'm here,
though, and might as well explain why."

He took a deep draught of coffee and resumed, "My son
Steve here wants to become a marine. His mother and I want
very much for him to do so. But he's been in trouble—with
the police among others—and I'm not at all sure that the
corps will have him. Whatever you do, do it on the boy's own
merits and not because his old man's a lieutenant colonel in
the Marine Corps Reserve."

Bowen nodded and turned to the younger Fletcher. "What
sort of jam did you get into, Steve? Anything serious?"

Steve tried to answer, but could only stammer incoherently,
"Well, I . . . I sort of . . ." It was the first time he'd tried to
talk about the accident with someone outside the family.
Shame reddened his face and made his hands moist with
perspiration. He squirmed in his chair.

"Here's the whole story, Sergeant Bowen." With that,
Steve's father took up the tale and recited, mercilessly and
completely, Steve's sorry performance during the last year.

As his father's account neared the episode of the wreck, Steve wanted to leap from his chair and run out of the room. He felt like blurting out that the last thing he wanted to do was to join the Marines. But he thought of reform school, of his father's threat, and that kept him silent.

Finally—and it seemed to be hours to Steve—his father finished the humiliating recital of the facts. "Well, Bowen, that's the record. Think you want him?"

Steve leaned forward on the edge of his chair and watched the marine's face for a clue as to what the answer would be. He wanted it to be "no," but remembered that the alternative to joining the Marines was worse.

The answer was not a simple one-word statement. "This is going to be a close one," the sergeant replied slowly, "and the close ones I buck on to district headquarters in San Francisco. Here's what I'll do: I'll give the boy his mental exams here this morning and this afternoon I'll send him over to the naval air station—they do our physicals over there—and have the Navy doctors look him over. Then I'll forward the results on to headquarters for a decision."

"How long will that take?" Mr. Fletcher asked.

Bowen thought a moment and replied, "We should be hearing in 3 or 4 days. Of course, I'll have to attach a special report to Steve's application, telling about his foul-up."

"Good enough," Steve's father responded. "Well, I've got a case in court this morning at 10:00. I'll leave my boy in your hands, Bowen."

"Fine, sir. Sorry that I couldn't say that all Steve would have to do is to get by the physical and mental exams, but . . . ."

"Forget it, Bowen, that's not your fault; it's his." As he spoke these words, Mr. Fletcher pointed to his son. He shook hands with the marine and strode out of the office.

Steve spent most of the rest of the morning filling out enlistment blanks and taking various kinds of written tests—arithmetic, vocabulary and mechanical aptitude. Steve didn't

care how well he did. Memories of the shame caused by his
father's revelation kept coming back to him.

That afternoon Sergeant Bowen drove him and three other
boys over to the naval air station. The four would-be recruits
rode in the back of a canopied pickup truck. Though the
wind made the canvas sides flap noisily, the three other boys
conversed in shouts. Steve kept to himself in a corner.

It was late in the afternoon when he got home. His mother
was in the kitchen, preparing dinner. He went out to see her
and, after giving her a dutiful kiss on the cheek, went up the
back stairs to his room. She did not ask for and he did not
give any account of what happened that day.

The next 3 days weighed heavily on Steve. The "Red
Rocket" had long since been sent to the junkyard, so he had
no chance to busy his hands and occupy his mind in the
garage. He spent some time with his brother, but Roger still
tired quickly and had to sleep a lot. Also, the sight of that
heavy cast and his brother's thin face and limbs made Steve
uncomfortable.

There was little to do but wait—with the mixed emotions
that he had about the Marine venture.

About the middle of the fourth afternoon while he was in
his room, lying on his bed brooding, Steve heard his mother
call from downstairs. "Steve, Steve, someone wants you on
the telephone."

He jumped to his feet and hurried from the room. "Who
is it, Ma?" he asked.

"I didn't recognize the boy's voice," she replied.

Steve grabbed the upstair's receiver, his heart racing. It
was not a boy's voice. It was a man's—Sergeant Bowen's.

Steve heard him say, "Just got the word from San Francisco, Steve. You're in!"

For a moment he was too startled to talk. Finally he
stammered, "Gee, Sergeant Bowen . . . that's, eh . . . swell."

He thought for a moment, then added, "When do I get sworn in?"

"Better come down here right now. I've got orders for you to report to district headquarters at 0800 Saturday morning. You'll take the oath there and leave that same morning by train for San Diego. That's kind of fast action, I know, but they've got a special car that day and it had one vacant seat. You got it."

Saturday! thought Steve. Why this is Thursday afternoon. That meant he had just one more day at home!

He spoke into the phone, "I'll be down right away to pick up my orders. Thanks." He put the receiver back and stood there motionless, a vacant expression on his face.

From then until Saturday morning it seemed to Steve that the hands of the clock raced like the "Red Rocket." Almost before he realized it, he was kissing his mother good-by on the front porch and getting into his father's car for the trip to San Francisco.

Steve was silent and pensive as his father drove down the driveway and out into the street. The house had almost been obscured by the cold, predawn fog before he worked up enough courage to turn his head for a last look. A troubling, unanswerable question came into his mind, What will happen to me before I see it again?

Neither Mr. Fletcher nor his son said much during the 2-hour drive. The October sun was already climbing into the heavens as they glided over the Golden Gate Bridge. Far beneath them in the bay, a long, gray ship—her decks crowded with uniformed men—headed out into the Pacific.

"What's that, Dad?" the boy inquired.

"Troopship. Read in the newspaper that the U.S.S. *General Meigs* leaves today with replacements for Marine outfits in the Pacific."

Steve recalled that Sergeant Bowen told him that Marine recruit training lasted 10 weeks. If he were lucky he would get a 2-week leave. Figures and dates revolved in his mind. As he calculated it, along about the middle or end of December he could very well be on a troopship himself, passing through the Golden Gate on his way to some Marine outpost.

"This is it." His father's words snapped Steve out of his embittered musings. "This 100 Harrison Street is a famous old Marine address. This is where you get off. If I went along in with you to watch you get sworn in, I'd just make you uncomfortable and embarrassed. Like a lot of the ceremonies you'll take part in during your Marine Corps career, the one this morning means something. Don't just join the Marines; be one. You can be, and a fine one, too. If you are, you'll be a man your mother and I will be proud of."

As he spoke these words, Mr. Fletcher was bringing the car to a stop in front of the Marine building. He leaned over, shook Steve's hand, and then snapped open the door for him. The boy hopped out, grabbed a small handbag which held his toilet articles, clean socks, T-shirt and shorts. With a short wave of his hand and a quick, "So long, Dad," Steve turned and walked across the sidewalk and up the stairs into the headquarters building.

It was only 7:30 but the hallway was already bustling with activity. Steve paused a moment and looked around, trying to get his bearings. Marines jostled past him, hurrying in and out of offices which flanked the hall.

Finally Steve noticed a sign over a door which read, "Recruits Report Here." He approached the room and walked in. It was already half filled with youths in assorted civilian garb. Some were sitting on benches which lined the room. Others were standing in small groups, talking. Steve looked around, trying to figure out what to do next.

"Lad, you in the detail gettin' sworn in today?" This question was asked in a loud roar and Steve jumped slightly. Turning around, he discovered that the big voice belonged to a small master sergeant who was seated at a desk. A placard on it read, "Benjamin Frankel, 1st Sergeant, USMC."

"Yes, I'm supposed to," Steve answered.

"Yes, *sir*," the little but ferocious man snapped back. "Give me your orders."

This stumped Steve for a moment. Then he remembered the mimeographed documents that Sergeant Bowen had given him back at the recruiting station. They were rolled up in his grip. He zipped it open, extracted them, and handed them to Sergeant Frankel.

"What you trying to do, roll cigarettes with your orders?" the sergeant asked in a voice filled with sarcasm and disgust. Steve heard the hum of conversation die down as the other boys in the room enjoyed the spectacle of the peppery little sergeant venting his scorn on a new victim.

"Sorry," Steve apologized.

"Sorry, *sir!*" the marine shouted.

"Sorry, sir," Steve complied meekly.

The first sergeant rifled through the sheaf of Steve's orders, stamping and initialing. He handed them back, saying, "Here. Take a seat over there. General Cross, just back from the Far East, is going to swear your bunch in this morning. Very privileged characters. I've been in this man's Marine Corps for 24 years, shipped over about six times, and I never been given the oath by no one but beardless lootenants."

Steve seated himself on the bench along the wall. For the next half hour or so he saw equally bewildered and hapless recruits get equally harsh treatment.

Promptly at 8 o'clock, a marine poked his head in the doorway and called to Sergeant Frankel, "Top, the general's here. He's topside in the old man's office."

"Okay, you guys. On your feet and follow me into the auditorium where the nuptial ceremonies will take place." The sergeant got up, and looking even more diminutive than he appeared when seated behind his desk, strutted down the hall. The soon-to-be-marines surged to their feet and followed him into a small auditorium at the end of the hall.

The sergeant hopped onto the stage. Facing the group he

said, "The general and Colonel Hudgins will come through
the same door you used. That means I'll see them first. When
I do, I'll shout, 'Attention!' and I want all hands to jump up
and stand as straight as your curved spines will let you."

Along with the rest, Steve sat down. Placing his handbag
underneath his chair, he tried to collect his thoughts.

"Ten-chun!"

The shouted command sent Steve and the others scrambling to their feet. Steve heard brisk footsteps. Turning
slightly he saw General Cross, a star on each shoulder, striding
down the aisle. The general vaulted onto the stage.

"At ease, men," he ordered, a kindly smile playing about
his eyes, "take your seats. I want to say a few words to you
before I swear you into the finest military outfit in the world."

The men sat down and the auditorium became as silent as
a tomb. Steve looked up at the general. He had never seen so
many campaign ribbons and decorations in his life. He had
never seen a general before, either.

Feet slightly apart, hands clasped behind his back, General
Cross began, "I welcomed the chance to come here this morning because I like to welcome men into the Marine Corps;
this is a big moment in your lives and I'm happy to be a part
of it. I also have sort of a special message. I had a regiment in
Korea where I saw your generation in action. Don't let anybody tell you differently—there's nothing wrong with you
'snuffies,' as we called you in Korea. The battle is still the
payoff, and I can tell you that your generation passed that
supreme test.

"But remember this—just joining the Marine Corps is not
enough. Be a marine."

Steve's mind went back to his father's advice in the car that
morning. Even the words were the same.

"Our enlistment standards are high," Steve heard the general say, "and that makes it hard to get into the corps. But the
real challenge will begin at boot camp down in San Diego. In
one way or the other, you'll be meeting that challenge every

day of your Marine life. Be a real marine—in character, conduct, dress, loyalty, faithfulness, efficiency. These are the qualities on which our beloved corps is built.

"Well, that's my speech. Stand now and follow me as I lead you in the enlistment oath."

The room was filled with the noise of scuffling feet and banging chair seats.

"Repeat after me," the general ordered. " 'I do . . .' "

It was now official. He was *Pvt. Stephen Fletcher, USMC.* Steve wondered if he were man enough to be a good marine. Can I even make the grade in boot camp? he pondered.

Chapter 5

"YOU'LL BE SOR-REE!"

AS soon as the enlistment ceremonies were over, Sergeant Frankel ordered the men to assemble in front of the building.

When they gathered out on the sidewalk, Frankel jumped up on a fire hydrant and shouted, "From here I'm marchin' you guys direct to the railroad station. There's seventy-one tickets, and two meal chits for each guy. I'll pass 'em out when I get you aboard the train. From then until ya reach 'Dago' around 0500 termorrow, you're on your own. But don't get no ideas about not gettin' there. General Randolph McCall Pate, of the Marine Corps and J. Edgar Hoover of the FBI personally hunts up A.W.O.L. boots. When they finds 'em, they eats 'em."

"How, Sarge?" a nervy but anonymous voice shouted from the rear.

"Bar—bee—cued," snapped back Frankel. "And no more of that wiseacre stuff, or I'll escort you to and through boot camp myself. Now form a column of twos—come on—column of twos, column of twos. You're marines now; act like it."

The doughty little sergeant hopped off his vantage point and ran about pressing the group out into two lines. Sounding the command, "Forward, harch!" he led the straggling columns on the half-mile hike to the station.

Steve enjoyed the march through downtown San Francisco. Policemen stopped traffic so they could cross busy intersections. Pedestrians stopped and stared; drivers slowed their cars to peer at them. Girls waved from office windows. One merchant, obviously familiar with Sergeant Frankel and the boys' destination, rushed out of his store and shouted to them as they passed, "Good luck, Marines. God bless you!"

As they marched along, Steve's attention was drawn to the boy who was beside him. He seemed too short to have been accepted by the Marine Corps. To keep up with the rest of the column, he had to take unnaturally long strides. Though small in stature, his nose was immense. He carried a battered cardboard suitcase, held together mainly by clothesline. He shifted the bulky case from one hand to the other. Seeing that the boy's burden was becoming increasingly cumbersome for him, Steve volunteered, "Help you with your suitcase?"

"No talking in ranks," was the boy's reply, whispered through his teeth.

This surprised Steve and made him slightly angry. But he said nothing the rest of the way to the station. His short partner managed to lug his heavy burden all the way without dropping it or putting it down.

As luck would have it, Sergeant Frankel, in directing seating, ordered Steve and his marching partner into adjoining seats. After throwing their luggage into the overhead rack, both boys dropped into the welcome seats.

His companion extended a hand and said, "I'm Bud Ajamian from Fresno. Thanks for offerin' to give me a hand back there, but I knew that I could make it."

"That's okay," Steve replied, grasping Bud's hand and shaking it. They both settled themselves, stretching their legs.

Steve was the first to speak again. "Say, where did you pick up that military stuff about not talkin' in ranks?"

"Ah, that's a kinda' long story!" the boy exclaimed with just a suggestion of a smile. "I'll tell you when Frankel gets through with us and the train gets rollin'."

Just then the big-voiced, little first sergeant bellowed for silence and passed down the aisle, making a last minute check of orders and handing out tickets and checks for lunch and supper to be eaten in the train's dining car. This completed, he called out, "Okay, Marines, you're on your own. No momma, no poppa, no Benny Frankel. Gung ho!" With a wave of his hand, he hurried from the car and disappeared in the crowd on the train platform. Steve was not the only one who felt just a bit sad.

In a minute or so Steve felt the train lurch ever so slightly. Then slowly, almost imperceptively, it began to move, pick up speed and pull out of the station.

His new adventure was getting closer!

For a while neither he nor his seat companion said anything. They peered out at the industrial panorama which was rolling by them or looked at the stream of passengers and vendors moving through the car.

After a time, when they had reached greener, more open country, Steve's companion spoke up. "You probably figured from my name, Ajamian, that I'm an Armenian. Ma's from the old country, and she's got the idea that from now on, I'm not going to get anything to eat. That satchel up there on the rack is filled with cheese, grapes, bread and a lot of other stuff. You gotta help me eat it."

With that he took the suitcase down. Steve, though he was anything but hungry, took a bunch of grapes and a hunk of hard bread.

As they munched, Bud spoke up quietly. "Guess I should explain why I gave you the word back there during the hike to the station. I was seventeen last August and ever since then I've been tryin' to enlist. I had troubles. First, I'm only 5 feet 2 inches. I had to get a physical waiver. Then my mother— my father's dead—wouldn't sign the release. Finally she gave her consent. I got sworn in. I'm still afraid, though, that something will happen. I won't believe I'm a marine until I get the uniform on. So when you began to talk, I got scared that the sarge might hear and send us back."

"Where did you find out that it was against the rule?"

Steve inquired, curious that a civilian would know such a rule.

"My brother was a marine. He sent me a book called *Guidebook for Marines*. It's got all that kind of stuff in it."

"Your brother's a marine? Where's he stationed now?" Steve asked.

Bud looked down at his feet and said nothing for a while. Steve realized that he had asked the wrong question.

Then Bud raised his head, turned to Steve, and said slowly, "My brother got killed over in Korea, at that big battle up near the Chosin Reservoir on November 29, 1950. He was a terrific guy; much bigger than me. But I'm goin' to try to be a good marine, too."

Steve listened, fascinated by this friendly little fellow who wanted to be a marine as much as he wanted *not* to be one. Bud, he realized, was a regular guy. One he could count on.

The two friends talked together, ate lunch, read and dozed. Soon it was evening and their train began to enter the outskirts of Los Angeles and to reduce speed. Then it came to a stop in the Los Angeles station, where they would have a 3-hour layover. Sergeant Frankel had warned them not to leave their car. A few adventurous boys did roam about the station, but soon returned. With the lights dimmed, most of the seventy-one marines went to sleep in their seats.

A few hours after midnight, the special Marine car was switched to another train and the last leg of the journey began. Steve slept soundly all the way.

"San Diego! San Diego! Last stop! Everybody off!" With these words, the lights were switched on and a conductor went up the aisle shaking any recruits who still slumbered.

The noise and bright lights woke Steve and he squinted out the window. The faint early morning light outlined a large and dirty station.

"What, no brass band to greet us?" was the shout of some undaunted wag. Most of the group felt sleepy and subdued.

Steve and Bud got up, shaking their heads and rubbing their eyes. They reached for their grips and then worked their way toward the door.

When they stepped down on the platform, Bud asked, "Well, where do we go from here?"

His question was quickly answered. "Marine recruits, fall in over here," came the shouted order from a dank arcade near the musty station. Steve looked closer and saw a uniformed figure there, waving a flashlight in slow circles over his head.

Both buddies hurried over to the marine; soon a large group had collected around him. After a muster had been taken to make sure that no one was missing, the recruits were herded into four, big canvas-topped trucks, about twenty to each vehicle.

The two boys, sticking together, clambered over the tailgate of the lead truck and plopped down on a slatted wooden bench, one of which lined each side of the long steel body.

"Where've I seen these things before?" Steve pondered out loud.

"These are old M-5's which the Marines have been usin' since the middle of World War II," Bud responded, surprising Steve once again with his knowledge about things Marine. "'Member when the papers and newsreels were full of pictures of the fight back from Chosin? The trucks in the pictures of the fight were these kind."

"That's where I saw them," Steve agreed. Through his mind flashed pictures of long columns of these very trucks, filled with dead, wounded and frostbitten marines making their way along frozen North Korean roads.

Would Steve Fletcher ever make a similar trek? He asked himself that question.

Suddenly the trucks' motors exploded to a start, shattering Steve's anxious mood. The truck behind them followed and then the other two. Soon they were moving along the deserted streets of downtown San Diego.

After what seemed to Steve to be a surprisingly short ride, the 4-truck convoy slowed and stopped. When he peeked through a hole in the tarpaulin, he saw a sentry box and a Marine guard who was inspecting the driver's credentials. The guard waved the truck through. The others followed the same procedure.

It was just about daybreak and the sun glistened on the dew-spattered tops of row after row of steel huts.

"Quonset huts," murmured Bud, who was peering out through a hole of his own. "There must be hundreds of 'em."

The convoy was united again after the delay at the sentry box. The trucks picked their way through the quonset-hut area and finally came to a halt on the edge of a huge parade ground.

"All out, you guys," the driver shouted through a flap in the canvas, "and take all your gear. I don't run no lost-and-found department."

As the men climbed or jumped out of the trucks, a lone figure observed them from the window of a nearby barracks. He shouted tauntingly, "You'll be sorry! You'll be sor-ree!"

As if by magic other marines appeared at doorways and windows. They took up the singsong chant, "You'll be sor-ree; you'll be sor-ree!"

Steve and his fellows were hearing the derisive cry of welcome which, for as long as can be remembered, has been used to greet newly arrived recruits at boot camp. And none shouted it with greater delight than recruits who had just completed training, and were shoving off to join their regular outfits.

The marine who had met them at the railroad station led the arrivals into a 2-storied building with red tile roof. As he straggled up the walk, Steve could see that three sides of a huge parade field—it seemed big enough to hold nine or ten football fields—were lined with buildings of Spanish Mission architecture, with columned arcades, red tile roofs, arched doors and windows and thick walls.

Steve noticed a sign in front of the building he was entering. It read, "Receiving Barracks."

The group followed its guide into a room already almost filled with recruits still in civilian clothing. "They're all yours, Swifteagle," the guide announced and left the room.

Steve looked at Swifteagle, puzzling over his strange name. He took a close look at the marine and the name puzzled him no longer.

Swifteagle, a tall, deep-chested man in his middle twenties was an American of Cherokee descent.

He looked the newcomers over and then spoke up in an even-toned, resonant voice, "I got room for twenty of you in this platoon I'm formin'." He counted down the line of men nearest him, "One, two, three . . ."

Steve was the twentieth man. To his distress, he saw that Bud, next to him, had not been included in Swifteagle's platoon. He was losing his buddy so quickly.

"The rest of you men file into that other room," Swifteagle ordered. "There's a receiving barracks sergeant in there and he'll take charge until they start to form another platoon."

"Sergeant, sir, I'd like to stay with your platoon." Steve, to his amazement, saw that this request was being made by Bud. The little fellow went on, "This guy here," pointing to Steve, "is my tombstone buddy."

Swifteagle smiled at the short recruit. "Well, feather merchant, you got a point there. Also, you're just about the size to make a good right guide for the platoon. There's no law that says there can't be sixty-one men in a recruit platoon. You're joined."

While the twenty-one new men took seats behind the forty already in the room, Platoon Sergeant Swifteagle paced impatiently back and forth in front of the room. When everybody was seated, he began, "You fellows are in this building for processing only. There are only a few things that have to be done here. The quicker you do them, the quicker you'll be in your own quonset hut, starting to get shaken down to Marine life.

"This is receiving barracks where you leave your civilian clothes, hair and life behind you. It's now 0545, 5:45, civilian time. Late chow goes at 0700 at our battalion mess hall. I intend to have all this processing over in time to take you to chow. That means you gotta move fast and move right."

Steve studied the marine. He wore three rows of campaign ribbons on a crisply pressed flannel shirt. His trousers were of that familiar Marine color, forest green. A sword, with its shiny brass handle showing, was sheathed in a scabbard which hung from a broad, black leather belt. On the desk behind him was a wide-brimmed campaign hat.

The garb of the fledglings was in sharp contrast to the sergeant's neat uniform. Most of the newcomers were wearing sport shirts of wild colors and exotic designs. A few others had shirts and ties. Steve thought that at least ten had been real cowboys; at least they dressed that way. Some of the group had short hair, but many like himself wore long hair, some in duck-tail cuts and other unusual styles. He suspected that two or three had even tinted their hair.

The drill instructor was holding up a piece of paper. "First of all, this next of kin form has got to be filled out," he explained. "Your official records won't arrive from recruiting headquarters for a day or so. We need the information on this form so that we'll know where to send your body if you decide to pass out right quick. Here, Lad, make sure that everyone in the room gets one of these." Swifteagle handed a stack of forms to a recruit sitting near him in the front row.

As the forms were being passed out, the drill instructor continued, "Any of you men sick? Don't be afraid to tell me. I repeat, don't be afraid to tell me. We got doctors and corpsmen here."

There was no response from the platoon.

"No sore throats, stomachs, ears? Okay, but if you guys ever feel sick at any time during the next 10 or 11 weeks, you're to let me know. If you're pulling a sham to goof off, the doctors here will spot you a mile off and I'll make you pay."

Steve got his form, and in the blank space labeled "Parents, wife or guardian," filled out his father's and mother's names, his home address and telephone number. When he was finished he looked around again at the boys in his platoon. They all seemed to be about his age. He wondered if any of them were married.

Sergeant Swifteagle had the completed forms collected and piled on the desk. This out of the way, he went on, "You guys joined the Marines because you thought you were men. Okay. That's the way you'll be treated. You're not mama's boy any longer. Boot camp is a complete change from one life to another. It's tough. But some 20 thousand men have already gone through it here this year and about the same number back on the east coast, at Parris Island, South Carolina. If you're any kind of a guy, you'll make it, too."

It seemed to Steve that the drill instructor was staring directly at him and that his words were meant especially for his ears.

"Now a few words before you get your 'bucket issue,'" Swifteagle continued. "See that trash can over there? I want you to file past it and drop in it any filthy books, pictures, dice, dope, intoxicating drinks, food, and so forth. Then pass by this table and drop off any knives, firearms or ammunition. If it's legal for you to have it, we'll take it and give it back to you when boot camp's over."

When this had been accomplished, he informed the group that its unit designation was to be "Platoon 164" and that it was part of the 1st Recruit Training Battalion, Marine Corps Recruit Depot, San Diego.

He then led the platoon from the classroom into a much larger room with a high ceiling. This, Steve discovered, was the supply room. As each man filed past a window, he was handed a large bucket filled with a towel, articles of clothing, soap, toothbrush, razor, blades, shoe polish, cloth and similar equipment.

After picking up the bucket, the members of Platoon 164 assembled at one end of the room where Swifteagle ordered them to strip to the waist and pull on gray sweat shirts that had been conveniently stacked on the top of the pile in the bucket. Steve looked around and saw that the group had become surprisingly homogeneous just by donning the sweat shirts.

Swifteagle then ordered the men to empty the rest of the bucket into a laundry bag which was now the top item on the pile. Steve realized as he filled the bag that he needn't have brought anything from home. In addition to the articles that he noticed when he first picked it up, the bucket issue contained stationery, shoe trees, nail clippers, swim trunks, pen, pencil, note pad, even a book of postage stamps.

"Okay, now we go topside to the barber shop," Swifteagle announced. "The only 24-hour a day, 7-day a week barber shop west of the LaSalle Street Station in Chicago." The men followed Swifteagle out of the supply room and up the stairs. They formed a double line at the door of a small room. As Steve walked by to take his position in the line, he looked in and saw two grinning barbers in the brightly lit room.

Swifteagle stationed himself in the hall, directly outside the barber shop. Steve, who was at about the middle of the column, waited anxiously for the first member of Platoon 164 to reappear. When he did, his appearance startled Steve. The recruit's hair had been completely shaved off, revealing a pale, white scalp. The victim was rubbing it, astonished.

"When you men have your haircuts, go into this room," Sergeant Swifteagle pointed to a room directly across the hall. "You'll be fitted for caps there. You'll need 'em. If you don't wear caps, the hot California sun will blister your heads."

Steve heard the two barbers guffaw loudly at the drill instructor's warning.

The double line moved swiftly. Steve could understand

why. It was no trick to clip a man's hair all off. Soon he was at the head of the line, looking in. Then a barber shouted, "Next," and he walked through the door and dropped into the chair.

Swifteagle looked in through the door. "Always can tell these California boys, can't you? Most of them have long, gorgeous, golden locks. Cutting their hair seems to break their hearts. But it's a quick way to cut the civilian out of them."

Steve felt the electric clippers run across his head, from the front straight back to the nape of his neck. The barber flicked a mass of blond hair on the floor. He resumed his clipping and cut another long swath. Then another and another, and Steve's hair cascaded to the floor.

Before he had a chance to settle in the chair, the barber was shouting, "Next" again and giving him a slight push out of the chair. The process had taken much less than a minute.

Stopping to look at himself in the mirror, he hardly recognized what he saw. He looked like a convict. He rubbed his hand across his scalp and it felt like a stubbled chin.

"Hey, Big Boy," Swifteagle barked at him from the hallway, "stop admiring yourself." The drill instructor glared at him as Steve hurried across the hall to get his Marine utility cap.

In a few minutes more the entire platoon had been shorn and outfitted with caps. The drill instructor led the men into a wash and shower room. "Everybody shave and shower," he ordered. "When you're through, take the same seats in the classroom you had when we were there before."

By the time Steve had finished showering and shaving, he began to feel better. For the first time since he'd left home he began to feel genuine hunger. He went downstairs and put his bucket and laundry bag next to the chair. His small overnight bag was under the chair.

When the last boy had returned to the room, it was 6:50. "It's 0650," Swifteagle declared, "and you men are too slow.

We've got to hurry if we're going to get to the mess hall before it closes. Outside on the double!"

The men jumped up and, grabbing their buckets and other belongings as best they could, ran from the room. Once outside on the parade ground, Swifteagle formed them into a platoon of four files, fifteen men to a file. Steve saw that Bud was out in front, all by himself. Each man had his bucket in his right hand and the laundry bag thrown over his left shoulder.

As Swifteagle was adjusting another file, Steve suddenly remembered that he had left his small grip under the chair in receiving barracks. He started to run in for it and had almost reached the door when he heard Swifteagle's deep voice boom out, "Hey, Lad, where do you think you're goin'?"

Steve stopped in his tracks and turned around to see the big drill instructor glaring angrily at him.

"I forgot my bag and was going back for it," he explained.

"Come here," Swifteagle ordered. He was standing in front of the platoon, campaign hat tipped back on his head and his hands on his hips.

Steve walked over to him and looked up defiantly. The drill instructor spoke in a low voice whose volume increased as he talked. "Never, never, never break ranks unless the platoon is dismissed or you receive a special order or permission. And stay on the beam. There are sixty-one guys in this platoon, and sixty of them remembered to bring out all their gear. You had to be the only knuckle-head. I should hang you by your heels for this."

Steve could hear titters of laughter coming from the platoon. His face began to burn with embarrassment.

Swifteagle turned away from him and faced the platoon, saying, "This man is a good example of an individual. Topside in the barber shop he stopped to admire himself in the mirror. Down here on the main deck he decides to wander back and pick up some gear he forgot. We got no room in the

Marine Corps for individuals. We're a team, a unit, a bunch of guys working together."

Returning to Steve once more, Swifteagle shouted, "Now get back in there, pick up your grip and be back in ranks in 30 seconds. We've got almost a half mile to the mess hall. If we're late, I know one recruit who is going to spend part of his first Sunday in the Marine Corps behind the range, a hot, greasy range in the mess hall. *Move out!*"

As Steve raced back into receiving barracks, his bucket hitting against his leg and his laundry bag bouncing around on his back, he heard the platoon break out in loud laughter.

Steve Fletcher had been in the Marine Corps less than a day, and in boot camp less than 3 hours. Already he had pulled two boners, one minor and one not so minor. He'd been caught and bawled out each time.

He realized that in the Marine Corps he couldn't make a mistake and get away with it. The corps was just like his father, maybe tougher.

What a terrible mistake he had made in joining the Marines. He hated it already.

Chapter 6

OFF ON THE WRONG FOOT

AS soon as Steve reappeared in the doorway with his bag, Swifteagle pointed toward the end of the platoon and commanded, "Fall in at the rear."

Steve hurried into ranks at the designated spot, glad to be inconspicuous again.

"Pla–tawn!" the drill instructor bellowed in a deep voice, using his belly, building up in volume so that its last syllable rippled across the parade ground and came echoing back.

"Ten-chun! Right face! For-ward, harch!" Platoon 164 surged down the roadway. As it did, Swifteagle began to call out the cadence in the flowing, singsong chant of the Marine Corps. "Lope, toodle lope, rye, lope toodle loaf." Steve soon found it was easy to translate . . . left, left, left, right, left, left. . . .

"All right, now step it up. Double time, harch!" With this command Swifteagle broke into a jog and swung his right arm in a wide arc as a signal for the platoon to speed up. Recruits at the head of the columns forged ahead while those toward the rear, unable to accelerate as quickly, fell behind. The platoon "accordioned" out along the roadway.

"Close it up. Close it up," ordered the drill instructor. "Forty inches back to breast; 40 inches back to breast." As he called out these corrections, he ran up and down the length of the platoon, his long legs carrying him effortlessly. "If you characters want breakfast, keep rolling. That chow line shuts down at 0700."

Steve, the last man in his squad, labored to keep in step with the drill instructor's cadence, "Lope, toodle lope, rye, lope toodle loaf." His handbag hung from his wrist. In the same hand he gripped his bucket. But the laundry bag that was slung over his other shoulder kept slipping off. The heavy bucket banged against his knee at every stride. Breakfast didn't seem half as appetizing as a slower pace would have been.

More like a semiorganized mob than a military formation, the platoon moved along the edge of the parade ground and then down a long street which cut through a quonset-hut area, and still they trotted at double time.

Just when Steve was wondering how much longer he could keep up, the platoon approached a long, low, T-shaped wooden building, and Swifteagle called out, "Okay, men, slow it down. Quick time, harch!" Then at normal marching pace, the platoon proceeded over a graveled surface to the wide front door of the building.

"Platoon, halt!" cried Swifteagle. "This is the mess hall. We're in time. Drop your gear in a neat pile by your right foot. You'll fall in by it after chow."

With sighs and exaggerated groans, the sixty-one recruits dropped their luggage, buckets and bags and filed through the double doors into the steamy mess hall. The drill instructor detailed one man to remain behind and stand guard over the piles of personal effects which made four surprisingly straight lines, marking the four squads of men and some newly acquired military order.

Steve kept close on the heels of the man in front of him as his platoon snaked through the door single file.

"Just what do you people want?" Asking the angry question was a heavy-set young man wearing the chef's hat and white uniform of a mess sergeant. As he stood in the middle of a wide passageway leading back to the galley, Steve could see behind him a row of broad stoves with wide, canopied hoods, a line of steam caldrons and other large-scale kitchen equipment. A cook was blending something in a large beater which looked big enough to be a concrete mixer.

The platoon stopped and all heads turned toward the rear to see where Swifteagle was and how he would cope with the aroused sergeant. The drill instructor was strolling down the line toward the sergeant, an amused smile on his face. "Morning, Bamford," he began. "Just formed a new platoon and I brought them over for morning chow."

"You're late!" the mess sergeant roared. "It's 0702; 2 minutes is 2 minutes. If it was any other drill instructor in the battalion but you, you big Indian, I'd run your platoon right out of here. But seeing's they're your papooses, I'll feed them. Tell them to pass down the line and pick up their trays, utensils and cereal. I'll get the galley crew to cook up some eggs and ham. Those guys back there are going to love you, Swifteagle; they thought they'd been secured."

The mess sergeant went back to the galley, and Platoon 164 followed its drill instructor through the chow line. Then, eight men to a table, they sat down for their first Marine Corps meal.

Although he was excited and uneasy, Steve Fletcher's appetite was good. He drank a glass of chilled pineapple juice. Messmen brought out milk, coffee, toast and apple butter and then showed the newcomers how to use the cereal box as a bowl. The novelty of this interested Steve.

By the time he had finished his cereal, the ham and eggs were being served. Steve ate two eggs and as many slices of the fried ham. Then he had some coffee and toast smeared with apple butter. After refilling his coffee mug, he pulled out a package of cigarettes and lit one up.

"Hey, Boot, snuff out that butt. Who said you could smoke?" Steve looked up and saw the mess sergeant.

"Nobody did," Steve responded. "I just like a cigarette after breakfast."

"Yeah? How about finger bowls to rinse your pinkies in?" the sergeant asked sarcastically.

Sergeant Swifteagle, who'd been sipping a cup of coffee at a table marked "Staff N.C.O.'s Only," got up and strode over to the controversy. Steve's heart sank.

"What's up?" the drill instructor asked.

"One of your recruits was about to enjoy his after-breakfast smoke."

"Which one?"

The mess sergeant pointed at Steve. "Him."

"Are you out of step again?" the Indian inquired disgustedly. "Sarge, I already had this ape booked to report to you today to do some of your dirty work, say riding the range. I was going to give him to you for 1 hour. Now it'll be 3."

Turning to Steve, Swifteagle said simply, "I'll see you later."

After all of the men had finished eating, they got up from their tables at the drill instructor's command and filed outside, falling in by their piles of gear. When they had picked up their luggage, laundry bags and buckets, Swifteagle called the platoon to attention and guided it back to the road which led from the parade ground.

As they marched down the macadam "grinder," the men of Platoon 164 once again heard the derisive shouts, "You'll be sor-ree. You'll be sor-ree. You'll be sor-ree," chanted tauntingly by groups of recruits leaning out of barracks windows.

The road continued through a sea of the sloped-roofed quonset huts. Every now and then streets led off the main artery, and down one of these Swifteagle took his platoon. He halted it at the very end of the byway, a "company street."

After unlocking the doors of one of two quonsets on either side of the street, the drill instructor ordered the platoon to fall out. "Take your gear inside one of these huts, pick yourself out a bunk, throw your gear on it and then fall in again here immediately. I'll make permanent billeting assignments according to squads. And I'll organize those as soon as you fall out."

The recruits hurried into the huts. Steve picked out an upper bunk and slung his gear up onto it. Turning to go outside he felt Bud Ajamian tug at the sleeve of his sweat shirt.

"Steve, what kind of marine are you trying to be?" His friend's face was clouded by a concerned look.

"Gosh, Bud," Steve replied, "I didn't mean to do those things. I just made mistakes and got caught. The D.I. has got me at the top of his list now but I'll work off it."

"That's the way," Bud grinned. "Say, let's you and me stick together out there," he said turning his head in the direction of the platoon formation. "Chances are good that way we'll end up in the same squad. Then we can bunk together."

By this time the other recruits had streamed out of the hut. The two ran outside and fell into ranks side by side.

Sergeant Swifteagle lined the entire platoon up in a single file and then rearranged it according to height, from tallest down to shortest, who was Bud Ajamian. The D.I. made squad leaders of the four tallest recruits. Behind each of these men, he placed recruits of gradually diminishing stature. Thus, the whole platoon presented an even, graduated appearance, tall in front sloping down toward the back.

This method of organizing the platoon obviously had frustrated Bud Ajamian's plan for encouraging the friendship. Steve, an even 6 feet, was the third man in the 4th squad. Not until all four squads had been formed was Bud assigned to a spot—all by himself in front of the 4th squad.

Steve concluded that this was the right guide's position, for which the drill instructor had selected the diminutive Armenian back at receiving barracks. Then it developed that for billeting and other administrative purposes, the right guide was considered part of the 4th squad. So Steve and Bud were not separated.

The 4th squad was assigned to a row of bunks in the same quonset where Fletcher and Ajamian had left their gear. The two picked out bunks and quickly emptied their belongings into locker boxes—wooden chests about the size of small trunks. A pair were under each set of bunks, one at the head, the other at the foot.

"How long will we stay in this same hut, Bud?" Steve asked.

"Until we go to Camp Matthews; that's the rifle range. That's at the end of our third or fourth week of training. I forget which."

As soon as the recruits had stowed their belongings, Sergeant Swifteagle marched the platoon over to the 1st Recruit Training Battalion supply shed to draw sheets, blankets and pillowcases. Each man signed for his bedding as it was given to him.

Back in the platoon area, Swifteagle gathered all his recruits into one hut for a lesson in Marine Corps bedmaking. "Start at the foot," he said, throwing a sheet over the pad. He deftly drew it tight and then showed the recruits how to make "hospital corners." He did the same with the second sheet and then with the blankets. To get the proper depth of the turnback of the blanket and sheet at the head, he measured the distance with his bayonet. One length.

The whole, impossibly precise job was done in what seemed to Steve to be less than a minute. "That's it," announced the drill instructor, straightening up. "Now here's the Marine Corp's test for a well-made rack." With that, he reached into his pocket and pulled out a 50-cent piece which he flipped onto the bed.

So tightly had Swifteagle drawn the blanket that the heavy coin bounced back into the air. A half-suppressed gasp went up from the platoon whose members, some kneeling, others standing, ringed the sample bed.

"Okay, you men turn to and make your sacks," Swifteagle ordered. The recruits scurried to their bunks.

"I'll take the upper one," Bud Ajamian told Steve as they

neared their bunks. "I'm smaller so it'll be easy for me to get in and out." The two men joined forces, first making the top sack and then the bottom one.

When they had finished, Steve took out a quarter. "Let's see if we got our blankets tight enough to bounce a coin," he suggested with a laugh. He tossed a quarter onto his blanket. It settled down gently. Bud's bed was equally limp. "Gives us something to shoot for," Steve declared. That reaction surprised him. He was beginning to respond to the challenges of boot camp!

As the men were finishing with their bunks, a bugle call resounded through the area. Swifteagle stuck his head in the doorway. "Church call. All men who want to go to church, fall out."

Steve hadn't even realized it was Sunday. He and Bud fell out and with the other recruits went to the church services of their choice, marching together with details of men from other platoons in the 1st Recruit Training Battalion.

As Bud and Steve entered the theater where their services were being held, the latter pointed to the tall flagpole on the edge of the parade ground. "What's that white triangular flag flying above the Stars and Stripes? I thought nothing ever flew above it."

"That's the church pennant," explained Bud. "That's the *only* thing that ever flies above our flag. That's a special American flag, too. It's much larger than the ordinary one and it's all silk."

When they got back to their hut after church it was time for Sunday dinner. The mess hall was now filled with recruits, the hum of conversation and the clatter of trays and utensils. Most of the recruits were in dungarees and field shoes, but some wore well-pressed green uniforms and highly polished, low-cut oxford shoes.

Their tanned faces, confident swagger and grown-out hair made it plain to Steve that these recruits had almost finished boot camp. He couldn't remember having envied or admired anyone as much as he did these almost-marines.

When he had marched Platoon 164 back from noon chow, Sergeant Swifteagle ordered all the recruits into one hut for a lesson in military courtesy and discipline. "Your training really doesn't begin 'till Wednesday," he explained. "There are 2 more days of processing, but there are a few things that you've got to learn right away.

"First of all, as recruits you are the lowest things in the Marine Corps, except for 'brig rats.' They aren't allowed to wear this globe and anchor insignia," he said pointing to the device on his campaign hat. "Neither are you.

"As long as you are in boot camp you will salute and say 'Sir' to any marine wearing this globe and anchor. You will stand at attention in their presence. You will, of course, salute all naval officers and there are a lot of them on this base. All doctors, dentists, chaplains, nurses serving the Marine Corps are naval personnel.

"Any questions?"

The drill instructor looked around at the recruits who sat attentively on bunks, locker boxes, and on the floor. When no hands were raised, Swifteagle resumed. "When the platoon is at ease, the first one to see a superior will shout, 'Attention.' That goes when you're inside too, like here. Sound off loud and clear. I want to see the overhead rise up a couple of inches every time I enter a hut. We'll try it."

With that, the drill instructor walked out of the hut and quickly reappeared in the doorway. The recruits stared at him, but the silence was deadly.

"You stupid apes!" Swifteagle roared. "Didn't you just hear me say that you're supposed to sound off the instant you see me? I'll try it again."

He left the hut once more. Steve inhaled and held his breath, waiting for Swifteagle to reappear in the door. Nothing happened.

This time the exacting drill instructor walked around the

hut and slipped in through the rear door. Fortunately one of the recruits at that end saw the door slowly open as Swifteagle entered.

"Attention!" shouted the boot in a squeaky but loud voice. The others came quickly to attention, jumping up from bunks and locker boxes, sliding down from the tops of the two-tiered racks.

"That's a little more like it," commented Swifteagle as he walked through the hut, looking over the recruits frozen in various positions of attention. "Most of you look like slobs but we'll take care of that later."

The lecture was over; the drill instructor told the men to break out the stationery which they'd been issued that morning at receiving barracks. "Write your folks," Swifteagle ordered. "Say you like boot camp, food's good and the drill instructor's okay. No bellyaching in letters home. If you write that kind of letters, your folks worry and pretty soon you begin worrying too."

Steve was bending over his locker box, trying to find his stationery when he heard his name being called. "Fletcher, Fletcher."

It was Swifteagle.

"Yes, sir," Steve acknowledged.

"Come here," the drill instructor ordered from the doorway.

Puzzled by Swifteagle's command, Steve threaded his way through the jumble of locker boxes and recruits toward the drill instructor. When he reached him, he came to attention as best he could.

"Fletcher, make your letter to your family short and sweet. You're one of those *individuals.*" He pronounced the word slowly and sarcastically. "We have no room in the Marine Corps for individuals. As soon as you've finished your letter, I'm taking you over to the galley for some exercise you need."

Steve returned to his bunk and hurriedly scribbled a note to his parents. Leaving it with Bud to mail, he found Swifteagle, who had returned to the drill instructors' quarters at the end of the company street.

Without another word the two went directly over to the mess hall. The sergeant who'd been in charge that morning was still on duty.

"I got that individual who needs some exercise, Sarge," Swifteagle said. "You remember, the boot who likes to smoke when the smoking lamp is out. Any ranges need riding?"

"No ranges, Chief, but a couple of greasy hoods that need scraping down bad," the cook replied, laughing and slapping his fat hips.

He led Steve into the galley and gave him a bucket filled with hot, soapy water, some rags and a tool that looked like a putty knife.

Pointing to the inside of a metal hood which canopied over a stove, the mess sergeant asked, "See that dust and grease?"

The inside of the cowl was coated. Steve could only reply, "Yes, sir."

"Well, get up there and scrape it off with this blade," the mess sergeant ordered. "Then wipe it down with the soap and water. I'll inspect when you're through. If it's not clean, you'll work on it until it is. On the double; all three hoods need doing."

"When he's finished, give me a ring down at Charley Company," Swifteagle broke in. "I'll come up and show him the way home."

Steve hopped up on the stove and began to scrape the greasy coating from the cowl's insides. The lower part went easily, but to get at the upper section he had to stand on his tiptoes. Here the canopy narrowed into a throat leading to an exhaust fan that blew the cooking fumes outside. The sticky mixture here was the thickest, and the scrapings dropped into his eyes and the top of his head, onto his face and hands.

Steve skidded and almost fell. What a way to begin boot camp, he thought bitterly.

When he finished scraping, he washed the hood down carefully with the hot, soapy water. After picking up the daubs that had dropped to the top of the stove, Steve went to the sergeant's tiny, crowded office and told him the first stove was ready for inspection.

"It's all right, Lad," the sergeant announced after his inspection. "Now turn to the next one."

His heart somewhat lighter, Steve started on the second stove. He repeated the arm-aching, backbreaking job. It too passed the sergeant's inspection. And so did the third.

While they waited for Sergeant Swifteagle to appear, the chief cook offered Steve some coffee and cake. "No thanks, Sergeant, I'm not in the mood for food right now, even that cake."

"Boot camp got you down already?" the sergeant inquired. "Stay loose. This is only the beginning. Wait 'till they really start throwing stuff at you. But the 1st is a good battalion and that drill instructor of yours is the best on the base. Why, his last four platoons have been honor ones."

"What's an honor platoon?" Steve asked, curiosity overcoming caution.

Before the sergeant could answer, the door pushed open and Swifteagle walked in. "What sort of job did he do?" was his immediate question.

"He cleaned the hoods up and got himself dirty. The kid'll do."

The big Indian turned to Steve. "Now, Fletcher, maybe you'll remember not to forget your gear and not to smoke until the smoking lamp is lit. When you get back to your hut, wash your cap and sweat shirt."

Bidding the mess sergeant good-by, Swifteagle led the way back to the quonset area in silence.

Without saying anything to the recruits who were sitting around inside the hut, writing letters or reading the manual, *Guidebook for Marines,* Steve got his soap and went outside to the open washrack where he scrubbed his cap and sweat shirt. Re-entering the hut, he held the wet clothes close to the stove and hoped that they would dry by supper.

As Steve stood there, Bud Ajamian came along. "Did you have to ride the range?" he asked.

"No, just clean the hoods of three big stoves," was Steve's reply.

"Steve, I can't figure you out. Didn't you remember what Swifteagle told us at receiving barracks about not smoking unless he tells us that the smoking lamp is lit?"

"Sure I remembered," Steve reported. "But smoking's a habit with me. I took a butt out and lit up without even thinking about it. I'll learn. I'll make the grade here. Tomorrow or the next day the D.I. will be on someone else's back. Swifteagle can't get me down."

Ajamian's face brightened. "That's the way to talk, like a real gung-ho marine," he said happily.

"Gung ho? What's that really mean?" Fletcher asked.

"Oh, that's an expression the famous Marine raider, Col. Evans Carlson, picked up in China. It used to mean 'work together,' but in the corps it's come to stand for a real, good, hard-charging marine."

"So that's what it means," Steve acknowledged with a laugh. But inwardly he was proud of his friend's new evaluation of him.

After an evening meal which passed without event, taps were sounded at 9:30, the lights doused and Steve soon slipped off to slumber.

"Hit the deck! Hit the deck!" Steve opened his eyes. The overhead lights were blinking on and off. He squinted at his wristwatch. It was 4:45. A different drill instructor, a corporal, stood in the doorway, shouting and flicking the light switch. Steve looked around and saw the other sleepers coming to life. He rolled out of bed and, suppressing a desire to light up a cigarette, began to dress.

After an early breakfast, Sergeant Swifteagle and his two-striped assistant marched the unit down to the quartermaster's warehouse. Waiting for them was a battery of marines behind a long counter who threw the recruits shorts, socks, T-shirts and dungarees. Then field shoes were carefully fitted and issued.

Returning to their huts, the recruits discarded their sweat shirts and multicolored civilian trousers and shoes. For the first time they were dressed like real marines.

Their drill instructors quickly marched them off again, this time to a large schooling shed which stood in a sandy area adjoining the parade ground. As the platoon stomped into the classroom, Steve looked up and saw a Marine officer, wearing the silver oak leaves of a lieutenant colonel, standing on the platform and observing them carefully.

When all the recruits had filed in and were standing quietly along the rows of benches, Swifteagle ordered, "Seats." The recruits dropped onto the benches. Steve contrasted this orderly episode with the noisy, pushing confusion which existed back at his high school.

The officer stepped toward the front of the platform and began, "My name is Lt. Col. W. E. Barton. I'm the commanding officer of your battalion, the 1st Recruit Training Battalion. It's a good outfit. We'll make you into good marines. Glad to have you aboard."

The classroom remained completely quiet. Steve stared at Barton and saw a light smile flicker around his eyes.

The officer continued, his voice deep and soft and slow. "You've heard that Marine recruit training is rough and tough. It is. But it's also fair. All of you are on an equal level here, different only insofar as the talents God gave you are different. You have left behind you the phony advantages and handicaps you had in civilian life. Is your old man rich? His money can buy you nothing here. Your family in high society? The only aristocracy we recognize is the elite of courage and character and accomplishment. You know a congressman? He may try to help you . . . but I'd better not find out about it."

He paused, cleared his voice and ran his hand back through his thinning hair before he resumed. "We are democratic but not a democracy. This is a point which sticks in most civilian craws.

"You'll be told when to go to bed, when to get up, what to wear, where and when to eat. Your commanding officer has authority over matters that used to be strictly your own business. But war is a weird experience. And the only reason that you are here . . . that I am here . . . the only reason that the Marine Corps exists . . . is to serve the nation in war.

"Discipline alone can equip men to triumph over the seemingly impossible conditions of battle. Fear can turn an outfit into a mob; only discipline can conquer fear. Here in boot camp you will learn prompt, exact execution of orders. You will learn teamwork so that you can work together with other marines to accomplish difficult tasks.

"Many of you will be on your way to outposts in the Pacific. Some will remain stateside. However, the foundation of this training is to forge men capable of acting in combat situations. If placed in combat you would know fear. Don't be ashamed of it. No sane man is free from it. Discipline and high morale will help you conquer it. By discipline I don't mean merely rules and regulations. I mean specific conduct in specific situations. Fire-control discipline. Water discipline. March discipline. To most of you those terms mean nothing now. In 10 weeks they will mean a lot—or we will have failed our job here.

"As for morale, you probably don't have a shred now. But in 10 weeks you will feel that Platoon 164 is the best outfit in the 1st Recruit Training Battalion and that the 1st Recruit Training Battalion is the best outfit in the Marine Corps and that the Marine Corps is the best outfit in the world.

That's morale, that's what they mean by Marine Corps *esprit de corps.*

"Marine Corps recruit training has proven what it can do. Now it's up to you to prove what you can do."

The battalion commander stopped talking and slowly surveyed the group. His glance moved along every row, lingered for a moment on every recruit's face.

Steve did not shrink from the scrutiny. What Lieutenant Colonel Barton had just said made sense. He sounded as if he were a fair man, a reasonable man, but also one who would deal swiftly and mercilessly with anyone who betrayed his principles. Steve hoped that he would never feel his ire.

"Any questions?" the battalion commander barked, shattering the silence. There were none.

"Sergeant Swifteagle, I turn your platoon back to you." With that Barton jumped off the platform and strode out of the classroom.

Well, now, thought Steve, this is it.

Chapter 7

SOME FRIENDSHIPS FORM

JUST as with those that followed, the rest of that first day soon blurred in Steve's consciousness. The platoon moved from one assignment to the other so swiftly that it hardly had time to finish one before being in the thick of another.

As soon as Lieutenant Colonel Barton had cleared the classroom, Sergeant Swifteagle herded the platoon outside and into formation. Stationing himself on one side of the unit and Corporal Gurdall, the assistant drill instructor, on the other, he aligned squads, corrected postures, straightened caps.

When the platoon had some order and uniformity, Swifteagle faced ahead and boomed, "For-ward, harch!"

Platoon 164 stepped out.

"Take the first step with your left foot, your left foot," both drill instructors bawled. Some of the recruits had begun with their right foot; others had used the left. Heads bobbed up and down irregularly.

"Pla–tawn, halt!" Swifteagle shouted. "From now on everyone begins with his left foot."

On the second try the platoon got off more uniformly. The two drill instructors marched along on either flank. Like tugboats nudging a steamer along a channel, they guided the platoon on its course—correcting, instructing, admonishing, insulting.

"Forty inches back to breast."

"Eyes directly on the back of the head of the man to your front."

"Chests out, bellies in, shoulders back."

"Keep those eyes off the deck."

"Take a 30-inch step. Don't goose-step. You joined the United States Marine Corps—not the storm troopers."

"Keep in step, you clumsy apes, keep in step!"

These commands were mixed in the flow of Swifteagle's rhythmically called cadence, "Lope, toodle lope, rye, lope, toodle loaf."

As he marched, Steve found it easier to keep in step. It was only when he concentrated too hard that he stumbled or bumped into somebody.

The 1st and 4th squads were on the outside flanks of the platoon with their members more exposed to the drill instructors' scrutiny. Corporal Gurdall supervised Steve's side of the platoon, and the latter was proud that he was one of the few recruits with whom the drill instructor found no major fault.

Platoon 164 marched across the sandy expanse dotted with training sheds, across the wide parade ground, through the central arcade and around a curving street. It neared a series of long, low, wooden buildings, painted yellow and trimmed with white.

From the corner of his eye, Steve saw a broad lawn, studded with palmetto trees and large hibiscus trees with red blossoms. As the unit drew abreast of the attractive setting, Swifteagle called out, "Pla–tawn, halt!"

The cluster of yellow stucco buildings housed the recruit medical and dental dispensaries. At the drill instructors' command, the men fell out and quickly formed a single line leading up the steps, across the porch and into the largest of the buildings. Jackets and T-shirts slung neatly over their right arms, the bare-chested boots waited.

Soon the line started to flow into the buildings. It was almost as if an automobile were moving down an assembly line.

Steve was worked on by batteries of doctors and medical corpsmen; his chest was X-rayed, his sight and hearing examined, a blood specimen taken from his right arm, several serums and vaccines inoculated into his left arm, his blood pressure taken, his heart and lungs checked.

The line moved through the building as the various examinations were administered by doctors and corpsmen in offices flanking the long hall.

Somewhere in the process Steve was weighed and measured. "Weight: 168, height: 6 feet $\frac{1}{8}$ inches," a medical corpsman called to another recording the statistics. "Lad," the sailor said poking Steve several times in the ribs with his index finger, "you'll beef out here. This Marine chow doesn't taste great—I can hardly swallow the stuff—but you'll get so hungry that you'll come to love it."

As Steve stepped off the scale, he started to question the garrulous gob but the latter shoved him along, shouting, "Next!" in a bored, disdainful voice.

Platoon 164 hadn't been completely processed when it was time to return to the 1st Battalion mess hall for noon chow. Under Corporal Gurdall's command, the unit came back to the medical center after lunch. Then in another building a new phase of the medical examination was begun. Here a team of psychiatrists and psychologists probed mental attitudes and capacities, trying to weed out the overly timid, the morally unfit and the weak- or sick-minded. Steve was pleased that no one in his platoon was stopped by these doctors.

By midafternoon the medical and dental examinations were completed. Except for an end-of-training physical check and remedial dental work needed by practically all of the recruits, one important phase of boot camp already was finished.

As soon as the last men had been cleared by the doctors and corpsmen, Corporal Gurdall marched the platoon to the parade ground. Sergeant Swifteagle quickly appeared there on the grinder.

The platoon began close-order drill, a painstaking rehearsal which continued for 2 hours until a bugle sounded the call for evening chow.

It was still light after supper and Sergeant Swifteagle, alone, marched the platoon to a long shed similar to the one in which the clothing and shoes had been issued that morning.

As the drill instructor disappeared into a lighted office at one end of the warehouse, mumbled protests arose from the platoon.

"These boondockers are murdering my feet. I got blisters on top of blisters," one man complained.

"Ain't the Marine Corps heard about the 8-hour day?" another questioned peevishly. "We've been going since before 5:00 and here it is after 7:00. And we're still not finished."

Steve looked at his watch. Its hands showed 7:15. Looking back at the events of the early morning, it was hard for him to realize that it was all the same day or that he had been in boot camp less than 2 days.

As for the memory of leaving home, that seemed separated from the present day by a vast span of time.

Suddenly Swifteagle stepped out of the shed. The angry hum quickly faded into silence. The D.I. surveyed the platoon, not saying a word. Then he spoke.

"You people have been marines long enough to know that there's no talking in ranks unless I give the order, 'Rest.' I only gave you, 'At ease.' That means no talking. Until you learn better, I'll keep you at attention. Furthermore, that's the way you should be right now. The first man who saw me coming out that door should have sounded off, called the platoon to attention.

"All right now, ten-chun."

After they snapped to attention, Swifteagle marched the platoon single file into the shed. It took Steve a little while to adjust his sight to the murky, barnlike interior. When he did, he was able to see row after row of wooden crates arranged on the floor. The tops on some near the door were open, and Steve peered into them.

Rifles! Each of the crates held a half-dozen M-1 rifles, Garands. There were enough in that armory for a small revolution.

An ordnance sergeant began to issue the weapons as soon as all the recruits were inside. Steve's turn to get his rifle came. Following instructions, he picked it up, read aloud the serial number stamped into its receiver, wrote this number on a receipt, signed this and turned it over to the ordnance quartermaster.

Carrying the weapon back to his place in ranks, Steve carefully hefted it. It seemed to weigh a lot more than the 5-pound .30-.30 Winchester he carried on hunting trips to the High Sierras with his father and brother Roger.

He rubbed the heel of his hand over the M-1's smooth, oily stock, smelled the pungent odor of the cowhide sling, checked the balance of the piece. It felt good in his hands.

When all the recruits had been issued rifles, the ordnance men issued bayonets, scabbards, cartridge belts, haversacks and knapsacks, and a small collapsible shovel, an entrenching tool. This equipment was piled on the floor in front of each man.

Rifle in hand, Steve surveyed the pile and wondered how he would be able to carry all of it back to the hut in one trip. Sergeant Swifteagle soon showed them how.

"Loosen your slings, your rifle slings," the Indian directed. He grabbed a rifle from a man near him and demonstrated. He adjusted the sling as if he were changing the tension on suspenders. When the sling was slack, Swifteagle held the rifle straight out in front of him. "Now put it over your right shoulder. Don't drop your rifle; you'll sleep with it if you do."

The drill instructor then showed the recruits how to attach bayonet scabbards and canteens to their cartridge belts and how to adjust this so that it fitted tightly.

"Now roll up the knapsack—it's the smaller one—and stuff

it into your haversack. That's the big one with suspender straps," Swifteagle ordered. After this had been done, the mess kit was packed in the haversack, the strips of which were tightened so the whole bulky pack could be slipped on quickly and easily.

A heavily burdened Platoon 164 marched out of the armory and back to its quonset-hut area. The sun had long since slipped down behind the Pacific, and a chill breeze from the ocean spilled across the training grounds.

When they were back inside the hut, Bud Ajamian stood close to the kerosene space heater, rubbing his hands together. "Gee, this heat feels good," he announced appreciatively. Once his chill was baked out, Bud joined Steve at their bunks. It was the first real chance to talk that they'd had all day.

"How you holding up, Fletch?" his buddy asked.

"Oh, so-so," Steve replied indifferently. "The Marine Corps sure keeps long hours. Why can't these drill instructors tell us what we're going to do next? They take us off for destinations unknown. I feel as if I'm walking the plank."

Bud's face broke into a grin. "That's part of the routine here. They'll hardly ever let us find out our schedule in advance; they'll keep us guessing. They want to wear us down. Same thing with the long hours. When he was a D.I. down here, my brother told me that during the first 10 days boots were kept in a state of shock and fear. They want to see how much we can take, and break us down to zero so that they can start building something."

Steve snapped back, "I'll take just as much as they can hand out. I didn't want to join this outfit but I'm going to be as gung ho as the rest. Even you."

"You can't lose that way, Steve. But want to see a guy who's heading for trouble?"

"Who?"

"Our squad leader. Dence I think his name is. He's from Texas and wants everybody to know it and stand clear. My brother used to say that noisy, big-mouthed guys are the ones who do the Marine Corps the most harm and get into the most trouble."

They both looked down at the end of the hut at the leader of the 4th squad. He was tall, lean and had a tanned face which contrasted vividly with the milky whiteness of his freshly shaved skull. While the other recruits in the hut busied themselves strapping their haversacks to the foot of their bunks, Dence stood in the aisle idly practicing the manual of arms with his newly acquired rifle.

He noticed that Steve and Bud were watching him as they made final adjustments on their packs. "You guys got your rucksacks hitched onto your beds?" Dence yelled above the hubbub which filled the hut. "How about coming down here and giving me a hand? I can't figure this thing out."

Before either one could respond, Corporal Gurdall stuck his head through the doorway and bawled out, "Platoon 164, on the road!"

Ajamian and Fletcher hurriedly tidied their bunks and straightened their haversacks and rifles, which were cradled in loops of tie-ties, white braided cord, hanging from the foot of the bed. "What in the world are they dragging us out for this time?" Steve complained. "At this time of night?"

Bud ignored the question and the two mates joined the rush of recruits swirling out of the hut and converging on the company street with their platoon's other two squads flowing out of the opposite quonset.

After some scrambling about for positions, Platoon 164 took shape, and Corporal Gurdall soon marched it off into the night.

Steve's puzzlement about their mission was quickly ended. The platoon pulled up in front of a lighted classroom. The recruits marched in and took seats. They had come to hear a lecture about GI life insurance and to fill out a form selecting a beneficiary who would be paid ten thousand dollars in the event of death.

Wondering whether they would ever have to claim the

money, Steve made his mother and father the joint benefi-
ciaries of his policy.

The lecture and subsequent paper work took more than an
hour. It was after 9 o'clock when the platoon got back to its
huts. Taps sounded soon after that. With very little noise,
the recruits pulled off their clothes and crept into bed.

"Are all the days going to be this long?" Steve asked Ajamian as the latter pulled himself up to the upper bunk.

"Longer," replied Bud with a laugh.

Steve doubled up the thin pillow and tried to get as comfortable as possible. However, even the coarse sheets, lumpy
mattress, hard springs proved no barrier to sleep.

Reveille the next morning came at 0500. Sergeant Swifteagle, who took the early muster, instructed the men to fall
out for early roll call every morning with both blankets and
sheets draped over their shoulders. This aired the bedding,
but of course it also made it more of a job to remake the bed.

After Sergeant Swifteagle marched the platoon back from
morning chow, Corporal Gurdall joined him. Both D.I.'s assigned cleanup details to the four squads. Steve saw the military system of passed-on authority in operation for the first
time. The drill instructors made each of the four squad leaders responsible for cleaning definite areas, both inside the
quonset huts and outside.

Billy Joe Dence, the 4th squad leader, quickly made it clear
to all that he was boss and very happy to have the role. Steve,
Bud, and another member of Steve's squad finished making
their own bunks and swabbed their portion of the deck, then
reported to the Texan for further instructions. He was leaning up against his bunk, a foot resting on his locker.

"You fellers follow me," he directed, walking toward the
door. When he had led them outside he pointed to the space
between their hut and next one in line. "Pick up all the trash
and make sure that you get any stuff that's blown under the
hut. Then rake the sand down nice and smooth. When you're

through, come on back and tell me so that I can inspect before you secure."

The three watched Dence disappear around the corner of the quonset. Steve was the first to say what all of them were thinking. "He sure takes himself seriously, doesn't he?"

"Yeah, but the corps will cut him down to size," Bud declared. Turning to the third member of the group he said, "Say, my name's Bud Ajamian. And this here is my buddy, Steve Fletcher. We're both from California, both from the San Fran section."

"I come from Gila Bend, Arizona," the recruit replied. " 'Gila' is spelled 'G-i-l-a.' It sounds like it was 'H-i-l-a' because in Spanish the *G's* are pronounced like *H's.* I'm Spanish-American myself. My name is Manuel Hernandez. Back at the Bend they call me Manny."

No handshaking formalized the introduction—the trio merely began to work. For Steve at least, the brief ceremony was pleasant; Manny Hernandez looked like a regular guy.

All over the sprawling hut area, recruits were busy policing up. Some, like Fletcher, Ajamian and Hernandez, scavenged paper and other trash. Others swept walks, cleaned "heads," dusted windows, whitewashed stones bordering walks. It was a busy scene, one that reminded Steve of a cutaway beehive he had once seen at a county fair—full of furious activity, yet all of it accomplishing something.

"Ain't you hombres done yet?" This challenge came in the raucous voice of the squad leader, Billy Joe Dence, who was standing, hands on hips, surveying the sandy strip between the two quonsets. The three had picked it clean and were now smoothing it down with three rakes.

"Lots of trash around this hut," Hernandez rejoined. "We'll be through in a minute. Keep your shirt on."

Dence flared. "Listen, Partner, just you watch out how you talk to me. I'm your squad leader, savvy? As long as I am, I'm your boss and I don't want no backlash." With that warning, Dence spun on his heel and walked back into the hut.

By the time the three had finished, the word was passed that the platoon was to fall out in 3 minutes. The trio hurried back to their bunk area.

"That's what I like about the Marine Corps—always plenty of time," Steve remarked sarcastically.

The hut was filled with busy, jostling recruits who tightened blankets and generally prepared their bunks and adjacent areas for the quarters inspection that they suspected would come while they were away.

"Platoon 164, on the road!" It was Corporal Gurdall who passed the word. Though he shouted it while standing in the middle of the company street, his voice reverberated in both huts. Recruits poured out the doors.

Under the spur of Corporal Gurdall's caustic comments, the platoon quickly formed and marched off. Literally hundreds of platoons from the eight training battalions were getting underway for the day's activities, though it was still before 7:00. The company streets, the roads and the training areas were full of platoons on the move.

After some brisk marching, Platoon 164 was halted by the assistant D.I. in front of a large one-story building. A wide sign, "Testing and Classification Center," hung over the double doors.

Steve's platoon was not the only one to be tested. Three others soon assembled on the concrete apron in front of the test center. Steve observed that these recruits looked as pale and confused as his platoon mates; their dungarees looked equally limp; their feet shuffled as clumsily in heavy boondockers. Observing the raw-looking, ill-at-ease youths, Steve remembered that his father had once told him, "There's nothing sadder-looking in the world than a new boot in the USMC."

After a brief wait outside, the recruits filed into the building, filled with long tables, divided down the middle and separated into compartments by foot-high boards. They took seats along both sides of the tables, each recruit having his

own fenced-off writing space whose boards served to frustrate any wayward glances during the exams.

The first part of the morning was devoted to intelligence tests, very similar to those Steve had taken in high school; mathematics, reading comprehension, spelling, history.

Next came the "dit-da" test to select men with keen hearing and reactions rapid enough to be trained as Morse code radio operators. Over headsets plugged into a socket at each desk, the recruits listened to a recording playing the two basic sounds of the Morse "alphabet"—dash-dot (—.) for "n" and dot-dash (.—) for "a."

The codes were repeated at an increasingly rapid rate, and the job of the recruits was to write down "a" or "n" as he heard it. For a while Steve could keep pace but then the signals started to come too rapidly and too mixed up. He dropped his pencil and looked around. To his surprise, a number of recruits were still listening intently and busily writing down the letters. Gradually, these men dropped out too. When the pace became too swift for all the men, the test ended.

This phase ended the morning part of the test. Steve looked at his wristwatch. It was 10:45. The tests had begun at 7:30. It hardly seemed possible to him that he'd spent more than 3 solid hours in that little stall. With muscles cramped by the long sitting and the exertions of the last few days, he and the other recruits shuffled outside.

Corporal Gurdall, who had helped proctor the tests, organized the platoon and marched it to the mess hall where Steve, Manny and Bud contrived to sit at the same table.

"How did it go?" Bud queried.

"Not bad," Steve replied. "But I couldn't figure out those pattern things. How's a guy supposed to be able to look at something on a piece of paper and tell what it looks like when it's folded up? What's that got to do with being a marine anyway?" he griped.

Obviously anxious to stem Steve's complaint, Bud Ajamian

turned to Manny Hernandez and asked, "What did you think of the test?"

The lad from Gila Bend smiled slightly, shrugged his shoulders and answered, "I guess that I did okay. The math was not too tough and I got quite a charge out of that dit-da radio test."

Right after chow the platoon fell in outside the mess hall, and Corporal Gurdall marched it back to the testing and classification center.

During the afternoon the recruits were given supplementary tests and were interviewed by classification specialists. Steve was impressed by these young marines, few higher than corporal in rank, who were intrusted with finding the right jobs for the right men. A very professional private first class interviewed Steve. At first Steve could think of no military occupational specialty that he would especially enjoy.

Then the interviewer asked him about his hobbies, and that reminded Steve of his hot-rod interest.

"Well, how about listing your first choice as tank driver, your second as amphibious truck driver and the third as just plain truck driver?" the Pfc. asked.

"They all sound pretty good to me," Fletcher answered.

"Okay, I'll put you down that way but you'll probably end up as an 0300."

"What's that?"

"Oh," the classifier answered with a slight laugh, "that's the MOS number for a rifleman. When the chips are down, that's the kind of marine the country needs most."

This news did nothing to brighten Steve's outlook.

It was well past midafternoon when the last member of Platoon 164 had completed the testing and classification process. Gurdall marched the unit back to the huts. As the platoon swung down the company street and neared its own quonsets, Steve saw that Sergeant Swifteagle was standing in the middle of the street, plainly awaiting the platoon with some impatience.

When they got closer to the drill instructor, Steve could see that his face was gripped in an angry, tight-lipped expression and that his dark-brown eyes burned with fury.

The Indian said nothing as Corporal Gurdall dismissed the platoon nor did he halt the recruits surging into their quonsets. Steve sensed that something was wrong. The instant he saw the inside of his hut, Steve immediately understood the source of Swifteagle's fury.

Every bunk but one had been ripped up. Sheets, mattresses, pillows, blankets were piled in disorderly heaps on the bunks. The only bunk that had been spared was the one over Steve's —the one belonging to Bud Ajamian.

The recruits stood around, wondering what was going to happen and when. They didn't have long to wait. Swifteagle strode into the hut, and someone near the door gathered his wits in time to shout, "Ten-chun!"

When the excited buzzing had quieted and the recruits were standing at ramrod attention, Sergeant Swifteagle began in a low, emphatic voice. "I showed you men how to make sacks the Marine Corps way. Today only one guy in this hut, only one guy in this whole platoon, had it right."

Steve caught Bud's eye and gave him a quick, congratulatory wink. Swifteagle's tirade resumed, "I want tight, regulation sacks and I'm prepared to spend the rest of the afternoon and all night here until every one of you apes has proved to me that you know how to make a sack my way. I'm not married and don't live ashore. I can spend the rest of the night here. Get started."

The drill instructor disappeared out the door and the hum of comments broke out anew. Steve walked disgustedly over to his bunk and began to untangle his bedding. He flopped the mattress into place and drew a sheet over it tightly, making sure that its corners were square and that not a wrinkle creased its expanse.

He plyed on another sheet and then a blanket. As Swifteagle had done the day before, Steve used a bayonet to measure the depth to which the blanket and top sheet were peeled back. He carefully made sharp hospital corners at the foot of the bed and then securely tucked in one entire side.

After walking around to the other side, he dropped to one knee and tucked the sheet and blanket in with his right hand while with the left he reached over to the other side and held it fast so that it would not be pulled loose in the tightening process. He stepped back to scan the blanket and pillow for wrinkles. Finding a certain slackness in the blanket, he leaned over and pulled it taut with two hands and stepped back for another inspection. This time the blanket appeared as tense as a drumhead. He flipped a quarter on it. The coin bounced back into the air.

"Real salty sack you got there," Bud Ajamian observed with a smile. He had been helping Manny Hernandez who slept in an upper bunk, harder than a lower to make.

"Think it'll pass Swifteagle's eagle eye?" Steve asked.

, The little Armenian shrugged his shoulders. "It sure should, but he's mad now and will be looking for every little thing."

By this time, most of the recruits had finished and were standing around, nervously reinspecting all the aspects of their handiwork. Suddenly someone whispered, "He's coming!" The men scurried to positions near the head of their bunks.

"Ten-chun!" a couple of men shouted in unison. Swifteagle strode in and began to inspect. Like the others, Steve was facing in toward the center of the hut. But by moving his head slightly and looking out of the corner of his eye he could observe the drill instructor going about his tasks.

Circling the bunk, he appeared to Steve to be looking for specific things, like a judge checking points of conformation at a horse show.

The first two bunks passed. But as soon as Swifteagle started on the third he snorted with disgust. With one rapid motion he ripped the bedclothing off, spun it around his fist until it had balled up and then flung it down on the mattress. The next few bunks escaped. Then three in succession failed. As Swifteagle worked his way down toward Steve, it became harder and harder for him to keep the drill instructor in his field of vision. By the time he reached Manny Hernandez' bunk just one tier away, the big Indian was no more than a blur in Steve's left eyeball.

Now Swifteagle was at the adjacent set of bunks. Steve subdued an urge to peek. He remained at stiff attention, head and eyes straight ahead.

Both neighboring bunks passed. The D.I. approached his; Steve's breath halted, his palms moistened with sweat. He realized that only his sack would be under scrutiny, Bud's having passed the original inspection.

The drill instructor's steps halted as he paused to give the bunk the once-over. Steve waited tensely. Then he heard the now-familiar twang of springs and the ripping sound.

His bunk had failed again.

Swifteagle strode silently on. He completed the row of bunks on Steve's side and began to work his way up the other side. He moved slowly, silently, steadily. Steve watched him and observed that the expression on his face remained almost constant. He did not hurry past one tier of bunks to linger over another. He said nothing. All that could be heard were his footfalls, the ripping up of beds and occasional nervous coughs by a recruit.

Not until he had finished did the D.I. halt to address the recruits. Standing in the doorway, his gaze swept down one row of recruits and up the other. It was not angry but so intense that Steve felt a sudden chill when the searching dark eyes focused on him.

"I'll be back in 10 minutes," the drill instructor announced quietly. "You people whose sacks passed, break out your

Guidebook for Marines and study Chapter 10. That's on drill for foot troops. Any of you other apes have any questions?"

Steve had one. He wanted to know why his sack had failed. He started to raise his hand but quickly stopped. He knew that the Marine Corps didn't operate that way, at least in boot camp.

Since no questions were asked, Swifteagle left the quonset.

Steve's bunk failed the next test, too. Finally on the following test it passed. Only Billy Joe Dence's bunk failed to get by that time. Then with the help and advice of practically every other recruit in the hut, the confident Texan was able to make his bed so that it withstood the drill instructor's inspection.

When Dence's sack passed, Swifteagle announced to the hut, "Now that all of you people know how to make sacks the Marine Corps' way, fall out for mail call."

Mail call! The words sent a wave of emotion through Steve. It was partly happiness at the prospect of hearing from home and partly fear that he would get no letter. For the first time he realized how much he missed home; the drill instructor's announcement had triggered a sudden flood of homesickness.

The first two squads of the platoon were waiting in formation on the company street. The men from the other hut had passed the bunk-making ordeal earlier.

Using the light from a nearby lamppost, Swifteagle began to read the names of those whose letters were among the slim packet and of those who shared the small pile of packages. As soon as Steve saw the scanty amount, he lost hope that his name would be called. After all, he mused, only 3 days had passed since he sent his address home. This hardly left time for his message to reach his parents 500 miles away and for them to get one back to him.

Swifteagle quickly instructed the recruits in the manner in which mail is distributed to boot platoons. At the instant a name is called, its owner takes one step backward, turns, runs toward the tail end of his squad, swings in a wide arc toward the drill instructor, cuts in front of him taking (but not snatching!) the missive on the fly and then continuing to circle around the platoon, resuming his place in ranks from the same direction that he'd left it.

Once the operation began to work smoothly, Swifteagle called off the names in rapid succession. A steady stream of recruits flew past him to return to ranks, happily clutching a letter or package. One complication arose. A recruit received four letters and by the time he had collected all four, he was breathless.

It was an amusing spectacle, but Steve watched Swifteagle closely and noticed that not a glimmer of a smile softened the Indian's stern features.

"Fletcher!" So intently had Steve been watching the scene— the drill instructor, the darting shadows of recruits hurrying in and out of ranks—that he had gradually lost contact with the mail call itself.

"Fletcher!" the drill instructor called a second time. Steve jumped into action and soon had gathered his letter and returned to his spot in the platoon. When the mail call was completed, Swifteagle dismissed the platoon except for those who had received packages. They would have to open them in his presence, so they followed him to the drill instructors' hut at the end of the street.

Jostling with the others, Steve hurried with his letter back to his quonset. He could tell by the handwriting on the envelope, a firm, simple script, that it was from his mother. He sat down on the edge of his bunk and ripped it open.

Everything at home was going well. His brother Roger was getting stronger each day. His father was busy, too busy with his practice to write right away but very anxious to hear from Steve and to find out about boot camp in the "new corps." Was it rugged? What kind of D.I.'s did he have?

His mother closed with news of the neighborhood and her usual quiet expressions of deep affection.

It was a simple letter and short. Steve read it through hurriedly first and then more slowly.

When he finished it the second time he inserted it into the envelope and stuffed the whole thing in the back pocket of his dungarees. Then he bent over and elaborately and slowly retied the laces of both shoes. This way no one could see how hard he was trying to keep from crying.

Chapter 8

A REAL NIGHTMARE

A
S the more rugged phases of boot camp came along, the
tempo of training increased. Steve noticed his civilian
past becoming more and more remote. Muscles tough-
ened under the pressure of long hours of close-order drill,
calisthenics and obstacle-course running.

An episode on the sixth day of training symbolized the final
severing of those civilian ties. Just after the platoon returned
from morning chow the junior D.I., Corporal Gurdall, ordered the recruits to pack up all their civilian clothes. When
they had done this, he marched them over to the recruit area
post office where the packages were mailed home.

When Steve shoved his carton across the post-office counter,
he felt as if he were abandoning his last link to the carefree,
outside world. He realized then he would have to be a marine;
there was no way out.

Boot camp began in earnest, and Steve saw that his outfit
was becoming, slowly but noticeably, a Marine platoon. It
couldn't yet march with the polish of the more seasoned recruit platoons he could see on the parade ground. But gone
were the fumbling and stumbling of the early days. Blisters
were healing; heavy boondockers became less clodlike.

Recruits were beginning to lose their feeling of strangeness,
to get to know one another by first names and to enjoy the
comradeship of squad mates and quonset-hut neighbors. The

friendships begun in the first few days became firmer, as Steve, Bud Ajamian and Manny Hernandez grew closer.

Another factor reinforced the trio's solidarity: Billy Joe Dence. The squad leader kept up his bullying tactics, singling out the three for all the heavy or dirty tasks. If a detail from the 4th squad had to be sent over to clean and swab 1st Battalion headquarters, Dence always "honored" Fletcher, Ajamian and Hernandez with the chore; if it became Dence's job to supervise the scrubbing out of Platoon 164's trash cans, the three knew who would get the wet, backbreaking job.

Steve's basic annoyance with boot camp stemmed from something more general than Dence's heckling, however. One night toward the end of the second week of training, he had a chance to vent his feelings for the first time.

With his two buddies, Steve was sitting around in the hut before taps, as they cleaned their M-1 rifles. Bud Ajamian unwittingly touched off the tirade by asking, "Fletch, what do you think about the Marine Corps? You didn't say much the first day I met you, coming down on the train from 'Frisco, but I got the idea that you weren't very happy about joining the Marines. How do you feel now?"

Steve put down the trigger housing group he'd been cleaning with a toothbrush. For a while he was silent—then he spoke up. "In some ways it's not as bad as I expected and in other ways worse."

"How's that?" asked Manny Hernandez.

"Well," explained Fletcher, "I thought that there'd be more rough stuff from the drill instructors. But so far I don't think that there's a guy in our whole platoon who's had a hand laid on him."

"No," Manny broke in with a laugh, "but when that big brave steps up close and looks you over, when you've goofed or something, it feels like he was slapping you over the head with the broad side of his saber."

"Boy, that's right!" little Ajamian agreed, chuckling. "But Swifteagle's 4.0. Gurdall's kind of a meatball, though."

Turning again to Steve he asked, "How's boot camp worse than you expected, Steve?"

"This place is too chicken," he responded in a tone of disgust.

"How so?" Ajamian inquired.

"Well, in a war, marines get shot up, killed by the dozen every day, go around unshaved, unwashed. They do a great job that way. But around this place they keep fussing around with parade-ground stuff. What good's close-order drill going to do us in combat?"

"Steve, you're looking at it wrong," Bud remonstrated. "They're not giving us all the drill to make parade-ground soldiers out of us. They're doing it to teach us how to be members of a tight team, how to respond quickly to orders."

Ajamian paused here and grinned slightly, "While I wouldn't want to attack a Commie pillbox in our parade-ground formation, you got to admit that it beats any other way of moving a large bunch of men from one place to another in a hurry."

Manny Hernandez put in his oar. "The best thing about boot camp is the way it builds up platoon spirit. Ever notice outfits just before they ship out? Boy, how they strut! They look good and they know it. That's the way I want to feel. That's why I joined the corps."

"A pair of squares, that's what you are," Steve observed in good-humored contempt. "As for me I don't get it. Why all this rushing around? Get here in time. Get there in time. Covers off. Covers on. Shave. Keep your top button buttoned. Don't talk in ranks. Smoking lamp is out. There's dust in the groove of your butt-plate-swivel-screw.

"And here's what beats me to a frazzle." Steve's manner became more intense, his voice louder. "You never get a good word if things are okay but those two D.I.'s of ours really lean on you when something's fouled up. *Now* I know where my old man got his ideas about discipline—the perfect is to be expected; anything less is a terrible offense against home and country. Why all the fussin' around here? This is boot camp, not combat."

Bud Ajamian jumped up and almost shouted, "That's the point! That's the point! We're learning habits here that we'll need in combat."

"What, for example?" Steve demanded.

"Teamwork, prompt obedience to orders, self-reliance. . . ." Here Bud hesitated.

"Okay, go on. Name some more," Steve taunted.

"Just a second, now, Fletcher," Manny Hernandez intervened. "We've only been here 2 weeks. Bud's not supposed to have all the answers already. But the most important thing that boot camp's supposed to do is to give you that old Marine Corps spirit. Look at those platoons just about to outpost and you'll see what I mean."

"Manny put it right, Steve," Bud observed. "We're here to learn the fundamentals, sure, but most of all we're here to learn to feel like marines."

"You guys got me outnumbered," Steve confessed. "Sure, it's okay here but don't expect me to get excited about the place or the corps. I didn't walk in—I was pushed."

Before the debate could be resolved, Corporal Gurdall stepped into the doorway of the hut and flicked the lights a couple of times. This signaled that taps would sound in 5 minutes, then lights would be doused. The three hurriedly reassembled their rifles and joined in the general preparation for going to bed.

Bud Ajamian enjoyed the brief, if heated, argument with Steve that was sandwiched into their crowded days. Bud had had few opportunities to talk with Steve about his negative, listless attitude. It troubled Bud to see his friend, basically a very likeable fellow, plod indifferently and at times resentfully through such an important and, to Bud, inspiring experience. He hoped the debate would help straighten Steve out.

Boot camp for Bud was often tiring and discouraging, but

its overall effect was a wonderful one, he thought. He was particularly stimulated by the increasing sharpness of their platoon. He couldn't understand any young American, least of all as nice a guy as Steve Fletcher, failing to get with it.

Then an incident which took place the Wednesday of their second week of training threatened to shake even Bud Ajamian's loyalty to the corps.

The day had been a long, hot and hard one, much of it spent on the obstacle and bayonet courses. In the afternoon they had concentrated on bayonet practice, charging padded dummies with fixed bayonets, plunging the blade into burlap-bagged "enemies."

Part of the practice required the recruit to parry a wooden shaft out of the way and then thrust the bayonet into the dummy's belly before heavy springs swung the hinged arm back "on guard."

On one assault Steve did not parry hard enough. As he charged in to plunge the bayonet home, the dummy's arm slapped back and hit him full in the mouth. The wooden shaft split both lips and loosened three or four teeth. Though the blow left him dizzy for 15 or 20 minutes, his pride kept him from reporting the humiliating experience.

At supper that night Steve could eat only soft foods. After the meal Sergeant Swifteagle took the platoon out to the parade ground for 2 hours of extra drill, smoothing out the rough spots.

It was well past 2100 before the drill instructor marched the platoon back to its hut area and dismissed it. Steve heaved an audible sigh of relief at the order, "Dismissed." He was bone-tired, his lips and mouth ached and he was slightly nauseated from blood he had swallowed.

Steve's only thoughts were the comforts of his bed, as he dragged himself between the rows of bunks. He grasped his rifle by the barrel and it trailed after him, bumping along the deck on its butt. When he got to his bunk, he fell into it and stretched out, his feet dangling over the edge.

"I've had it," was his admission.

Bud Ajamian had pulled his locker box out from under the bunk and sat on it while he unlaced his shoes. "Don't fade away, Steve," he warned, "or you'll wake up and it'll be tomorrow morning."

"Good. Then I won't have to get dressed again," Steve replied with a weak laugh.

"Yeah, but you'll never get any decent sleep with your clothes on and besides, you should wash your mouth and lips. They're puffed pretty bad."

That made sense to Steve and he pulled himself up. After slinging his M-1 in the loops at the foot of his bunk, he made his way slowly to the wash hut. When he returned, he wearily undressed. Letting the clothes lie where they fell, he crept between the sheets.

Steve made a try at his brief nightly prayer in which he asked the Lord to protect his father and his mother, his brother and himself. Before he could finish it, his eyes fluttered shut. He slept.

Later on in their many post-mortem discussions about the wild night, the recruits had conflicting memories of how it began. The first thing that Steve remembered was the lights suddenly being switched on. He then heard a loud, coarse voice. "I want every one of you guys on the road in 2 minutes, fully dressed and carrying your bucket and sea bag."

At first Steve thought he was having a bad dream. He sat upright in bed, shaking his head to clear his vision and squinting at his wristwatch. It was 1:20 a.m. He looked around and saw that most of the other recruits were sitting up, some even starting to dress.

"Hit the deck!" the voice in the doorway bawled out. Steve peered and saw Corporal Gurdall giving the orders, clad in his dress blue uniform but hatless.

Bud Ajamian dangled over the edge of his bunk and slid to the deck. "Rise and shine, Steve," he said sleepily. "This is no dream."

"What gives?" Steve asked.

Bud scratched his head in mystification. "Beats me. Looks like Gurdall has just come in off liberty and had too many beers. But it could be a real emergency. Maybe Russia's declared war."

"Why the bucket?" Steve inquired.

"To hold our tears. Now get out of bed," Bud blurted out a bit angrily. "I don't know anything more about this than you do!"

Steve pushed himself out of bed, groped for his dungarees and started to dress. He was still lacing his boondockers when Gurdall reappeared to shout, "Platoon 164, on the road!"

With shoelaces dragging and clothes flapping, Steve joined the line of puzzled recruits hurrying out into the darkness. Like the others, he had a bucket in one hand and a sea bag, hastily dug out of his locker box, in the other.

The recruits were streaming out of the other hut, too. Corporal Gurdall, still hatless, stood in the shadows, watching. When the ranks were filled, he stepped forward and in a hoarse whisper announced, "This is a special night exercise. Silence must be maintained. You've already done something wrong. I ordered you to fall out with sea bags full." (He hadn't.) "Go back and stuff your pillow and blankets into them. Quietly!"

Silently the recruits broke ranks and disappeared into the huts. They soon reappeared, struggling with bulging bags.

When the platoon had formed again, the junior D.I. did not take the familiar route up the company street. Instead he marched it a short distance to the end of the street and out across an unpaved path that led to sandy wastes at the rear of the obstacle and bayonet courses.

As the platoon drew away from the hut areas and into more and more remote regions, Steve, now wide awake, noticed that the corporal's voice grew louder and louder. It occurred to Steve that the drill instructor had muted his voice so that he would not be discovered taking the platoon off on this exercise, an unauthorized expedition. Bud's theory about the beers made sense. The fact that the sentry was left behind in the area—the first case of such an omission—also indicated that Gurdall had taken great pains to escape being detected.

The moon wasn't full but a clear, cloudless sky permitted what moonlight there was to stream down unfiltered. Gurdall, the collar of his tunic now unbuttoned, stumbled over the rough ground. In the distance Steve could see the main buildings of the base outlined in the moonlight. So quiet was the night that the ship's bell of an aircraft carrier moored nearby in the harbor could be heard tolling three times, indicating that it was 1:30.

The recruits struggled on, bucket in one hand, sea bag slung over the other shoulder. Few of them had been able to dress fully; their loose shoelaces lashed about, tripping them; their unbuttoned dungaree coats flapped in the chill air and their pants slipped down.

Gurdall had yet to indicate where he was going, but his occasional orders to change direction made it plain that he did have a destination in mind.

"All right, you feather merchants, double time, *March!*" he suddenly blurted out. As best it could, the platoon broke into a trot. Men slipped in the loose sand, which collected rapidly in their unlaced shoes. Gurdall cursed the stumblers. After a long run they reached a secluded spot, shielded from observation by a line of low storage sheds. Here the drill instructor halted the platoon.

Ordering a facing movement so that the platoon fronted him, Gurdall began, "I got you knuckle-heads out here because I wanted to show you what punks you are. I know what you think. You rate that big, stupid Indian a better marine than me. You're wrong. And before we leave here tonight, each one of you apes is going to come front and center and tell me that I'm the greatest marine you know or ever will know."

Steve, in the rank closest to the drill instructor, could observe the man closely. Though Gurdall's feet were spread wide apart, he was so drunk that he teetered back and forth. His hands were on his hips. The moonlight struck his features and cast grotesque shadows down his face, not a handsome one at best.

While the perspiring platoon shivered in the chilly breeze blowing in off the bay, the drill instructor rambled on incoherently, boasting, swearing, threatening.

He paused, as if to decide what his next course of action would be. Then he shouted, "You idiots have learned the manual of arms with the M-1 rifle; now you're going to do it with sea bags, with the bucket on your head! Okay, place the bucket on your head."

The recruits exchanged puzzled glances.

"What are you waiting on?" Gurdall screamed in a high-pitched whine. "Your bucket's your helmet. Wear it!"

Seeing that the drill instructor indeed meant what he said, the recruits raised their buckets to their heads and gingerly slipped them on. Steve lowered his pail with both hands. It came down completely over his head, its rim resting on his shoulders. In that position the bucket wobbled to and fro. He spun it around until the handle was under his chin, like the strap on a guardsman's shako.

"Fletcher over there's got the right idea—put the handle under your chin." Steve was surprised that the D.I. had been watching him that closely. He himself could hardly see more than the ground upon which he stood. The bucket-helmet also muffled hearing.

"Prepare to do the manual of sea bags."

That weird command filled Steve with confusion. "Manual of sea bags," he muttered to himself. "What in heaven's name could that be?"

Gurdall coughed and cleared his throat. "You men have been in the Marine Corps long enough to learn the manual of arms. Manual of sea bags is the same thing; you just use sea bags instead of rifles.

"I want it done smartly, with precision. Snap that sea bag around. The first man to drop his piece will know how my size 11 low-cuts feel in the seat of his butt. The second man will know two times. And so forth."

Gurdall's wild speech left him breathless. He took a gasp of air and resumed. "You'll never do manual of the sea bags on the grinder, but it'll help make marines out of the sorriest platoon to hit this base ever.

"All right, left shoulder, arms! For-ward, harch!"

Steve groped for his sea bag with both hands. He found it after some search and hurriedly threw it over his shoulder. But before he could take a step, the man to his rear pushed into him.

"Sorry, Steve," the offender whispered loudly. Steve recognized the voice as that of Big Jawn Gillyard, an athletic Negro boy from Chicago. He smiled to himself.

In four lines abreast, the platoon swept over the nubby terrain. After marching this way for a while, Gurdall shouted, "By the right flank, harch!" This command not only changed the direction of march 90° but transposed the platoon into four squads, each in a single file.

"Right shoulder, arms!" was the drill instructor's next command. Steve clumsily shifted the sea bag from his left shoulder to his right. He attempted nothing precise; all he wanted to do was to avoid dropping the bulging pouch.

"What's the matter, Slippery Fingers? Can't you hold onto it?" Steve heard the thud of a foot hitting someone near him and the victim's instinctive reaction, "Ouch!"

"Pick up your bag and fall in at the end of your squad," Gurdall ordered his victim.

The exertion of marching over the uneven, sandy soil while shifting the awkward bag about began to tell on Steve. His breath came faster, resounding in the pail. This made it harder to catch the commands, which were becoming more frequent.

It was impossible to see Gurdall, but from the sound of his

voice he appeared to be shifting his position around the platoon. Steve heard it first on one side, then on the other, up in front of the platoon, then down at the rear.

At almost every command some recruit would drop his sea bag. True to his warning, Gurdall punished the offenders with a series of kicks. Once or twice Steve dropped his bag. He gritted his teeth and stiffened himself for the blows. Neither time did they come. He snatched up his bag, more than slightly happy that his failure had gone undiscovered.

In reliving the episode later, few in the platoon could agree on the length of time spent tramping up and down. Bud Ajamian thought that it was 15 or 20 minutes. Others thought it as long as an hour.

At the time, it seemed to Steve to be a nightmare with no end. He breathed in short, rapid pants; perspiration oozed down his face, stinging his bruised lips; his arms and shoulders ached; sand, it felt like a shovelful, had worked its way into both shoes. To try to see where he was going, Steve pressed his chin to his chest and concentrated on the small area of visibility in front of his feet.

Invariably he saw obstacles too late to avoid them. Much of the time he spent stumbling over a hillock, a tuft of march grass or a fallen sea bag.

Then he began to feel that he couldn't stand it much longer. But so far as he could figure out, no one yet had quit. Steve was determined to hold on as long as he had strength. He certainly would not be the first to fall out.

So he stumbled along, shifting his sea bag from shoulder to shoulder at the commands. It seemed to him that he had long since exhausted all his energy, that he was now going on nerve alone.

At last Gurdall called a halt. "Take off your helmets," he ordered with a sardonic laugh. The weary recruits let their sea bags drop and lifted off their pails. Steve had to blink to accustom his eyes to the pale moonlight. As his vision sharpened he could see that the platoon was strung out over an area nearly three times the size it ordinarily occupied when in formation.

"Ragged platoon," Gurdall spat disgustedly. "Been in boot camp going on 3 weeks and still can't march. Cover down and dress it up."

The recruits tightened and aligned their formation. "That's better," the drill instructor observed. "Now I'm ready for volunteers. Who's going to be the first to come front and center and admit that I'm the best D.I., the best marine you know or ever will know?"

Not a man in Platoon 164 moved. Fletcher was close enough to the drill instructor to see the muscles in his face grow taut and his eyes narrow to angry little slits. His dress blue uniform appeared to be even more disheveled from the drill. Cockleburs speckled the bottom of his pants.

"Need some more persuading? I got plenty of time and intend to make myself comfortable. Here, you scum of the 4th squad, peel off and dump your sea bags in a pile in front of me."

The men in Steve's squad, which had been the one nearest to the drill instructor, piled their sea bags in the designated spot. "Crisscross them and put a few at this end," Gurdall directed; "you feather merchants are putting together a mattress for me. Make it soft!"

When a pair of recruits had rearranged the heap, Gurdall climbed onto it and ensconced himself, his head pillowed by a pair of sea bags, his legs spread out comfortably.

Thus snugly settled, he resumed his talk. "Since you were a little slow to make up your minds and since I'm a little tired, I'm going to rack out here while you boys sing my favorite song. How many know 'Good Night, Irene'?"

A few scattered voices broke the silence.

"Good, that's plenty. Those that don't know will listen and learn. I want to hear it real loud. Okay, begin. Just a minute, just a minute. Put your buckets back on; that way you'll be able to hear yourselves better."

Steve reached over and placed the bucket back on his head. It appeared that the chill night air had sobered Gurdall somewhat. His voice was less thick and his speech was faster. But where the alcohol had worn off, the essential ugliness of the bully replaced it.

Steve wondered how much longer the madness would go on and how it would all end.

"Now all begin," the drill instructor said. "One, two, three!"

> Good night, Irene, good night,
> I'll see you in my dreams.*

Thus the recruits sang the rather pathetic song through. As soon as they had finished one verse, Gurdall ordered another. From time to time he would get up, walk over to some unsuspecting recruit and kick him sharply in the shins, shouting, "You're not loud enough. Sing out, Sweet Lips." This time Steve was one of his victims.

The platoon went on, singing chorus after monotonous chorus. Steve's voice grew hoarse and broke. His mouth ached and his thirst was acute. But he and the others kept it up, roaring the song into the buckets so loud and long that their ears rang.

Perhaps it was the deafened ears or maybe just concentration on the song. Whatever the explanation, Steve suddenly became aware that he was the only one still singing. He stopped and listened.

Someone was talking quite harshly to Gurdall. Steve at first thought that some recruit had cracked under the strain and was berating Gurdall.

Steve listened more intently. That voice was not that of any recruit. It was Swifteagle's! Steve yanked his bucket off to see what had developed.

Sergeant Swifteagle and two other marines, one a first or second lieutenant, had Gurdall collared. While Swifteagle

---

* Words and Music by Huddie Ledbetter and John Lomax. Copyright 1936 by Ludlow Music, Inc.

and the officer questioned Gurdall, the third man played a flashlight on his face.

The voices, first loud, quieted. Gurdall was saying nothing. Then Steve heard the officer. "Let's not keep the boots out here any longer. Take them back to their huts, Sergeant. I'll take this guy to the depot officer of the day and see to it that he ends up at the brig."

The lieutenant turned to Gurdall. "Corporal, you're a disgrace to your uniform," he snarled. "You're under arrest. March in front of me. On the straight and narrow. This .45 I have in my hand here has a round in the chamber with your name on it! Forward, harch!"

For the first time Steve noticed that the lieutenant held a pistol in his hand, its short, burnished snout glistening in the moonlight.

Sergeant Swifteagle lost little time in calling the platoon to attention. Without an unnecessary word, he started the platoon on its long hike back to the quonsets.

As they marched away from the scene of the ordeal, Steve saw the lights of a jeep flash on. Gurdall was on the trail ahead of it, caught in the headlights' bright glare.

The lieutenant, his pistol still at the ready, was standing up, peering out over the windshield of the topless vehicle.

The jeep started and Gurdall lurched along about 10 feet in front. The car bounced slowly over the rough path, following the disgraced marine like an angry watchdog herding in a criminal.

Chapter 9

RED MIKE'S DESTINATION

NOT until well after 3 a.m. were the members of Platoon 164 showered and back under the covers. As the men readied for bed a second time, they wondered if they would be allowed to "sleep in" the next morning. Fletcher predicted that the hazing episode would have no effect.

Morning reveille proved him right. Promptly at 0515 the sentry on duty snapped on the overhead lights. With a chorus of groans, the quonset came to life. The recruits ripped up their beds and with blankets and sheets on their shoulders stumbled out like zombies for morning muster.

Sergeant Swifteagle was on deck, and he marched the platoon to morning chow at the scheduled time. The only reference the recruits ever heard him make to the night's abusive experience came just before he dismissed them to enter the mess hall. "Don't say anything to anybody about what happened last night. You can be sure that Gurdall will get what's coming to him."

That directive was, of course, completely, if cautiously, ignored. Word of the ordeal had preceded Platoon 164 to the mess hall, and Steve and his fellow recruits were the object of much curious questioning.

This curiosity persisted until the platoon had completed boot camp and was disbanded. During the rare occasions

when the men were in unsupervised contact with other recruits, the midnight "exercise" would always come up. "Platoon 164? Wasn't your outfit the one that had the D.I. who
went 'Asiatic'? Give us the scoop, huh?"

During the day following the ordeal, all four squad leaders
were questioned by provost marshal special investigators. So
was Bud Ajamian, as the platoon's right guide. Toward the
end of boot camp, after returning from the rifle range, these
same men testified at the court-martial. And just before the
platoon shipped out, the men were to learn the sentence given
the corporal for his abuse of authority.

For a day or two after Gurdall's moonlight expedition,
Sergeant Swifteagle performed all the drill instructor's chores
singlehandedly. Then a relief for Gurdall arrived, another
corporal, R. Y. Bailey, a tall, slim Virginian, whose face bore
a vivid red scar that ran across his right cheek and disappeared in the hair above his ear.

The platoon grapevine soon was passing the word that
Bailey had been wounded by a Communist mortar fragment
in the fighting around the "iron triangle" north of Seoul,
Korea. Unlike most boot camp rumors, however, this report
proved to be correct.

Bailey soon proved to the platoon that he was a fit partner
for Swifteagle—quiet, competent, a relentless perfectionist,
remote, severe but fair. The two drove the platoon tirelessly
—to classrooms, field demonstrations, through dozens of irksome but essential administrative chores, drilling it on the
parade ground, hour after hour, day after day, getting it up
in the early hours, putting it to bed late in the chill, foggy,
fall evenings.

Steve Fletcher became more and more impatient with the
incessant pressure and the demand for precision in everything. There was too much happening for him to be bored,
but he grew very apathetic and tired. The time passed fast
enough but the day got underway so early that by taps it often

seemed to Steve that not one day but two had passed since he'd gotten up that morning. The constant activity irked Steve, too, because it left no chance for a quiet smoke off by himself, daydreaming or just killing time.

Somewhat to Steve's surprise, Swifteagle had not made him a special target despite his misadventures on that first day. Much about the platoon during its early weeks was fumbling and inept. Fletcher's lack of interest was concealed amid the platoon's general clumsiness.

But as 164 became a more organized platoon, some minor incidents occurred which alerted Steve to the fact that both Swifteagle and Bailey knew who the dolts were—and that they had him tagged as one.

Then toward the end of the third week of training an incident happened which made Fletcher a marked man and which threatened to leave a black mark on his whole Marine Corps record.

The training schedule called for a rifle and personnel inspection by the battalion commander's staff, to take place in the first of the daily instruction periods, beginning at 0730. The drill instructors this time passed the word so that the recruits could clean their rifles and ready their clothes. The hour just before taps was left free for this purpose.

Steve, however, felt sleepy. Ignoring the pleas of Bud and Manny Hernandez, he crawled into his bunk.

"I'll get at it right after chow tomorrow. There'll be plenty of time. No calisthenics before a battalion inspection," he argued, pulling his blankets over his head to shut out the light from the row of lamps dangling from the center of the bell-shaped hut.

Soon he was sleeping soundly.

The next thing Steve knew the lights were being flicked on and off and Swifteagle was shouting, "All right, you people. Hit the deck. Fall out immediately for physical drill with arms."

Steve sat up in bed, trying to figure out what there was about the D.I.'s order that disturbed him so. As he sat there pondering, the brown, muscled, hairy leg of Bud Ajamian dangled over the edge of the bunk above.

Bud slid to the floor. "Steve, you've got no time to lose," he advised earnestly. "Did you hear what Swifteagle just said? We're going out for physical drill this morning. That means you'll hardly have any time to work on your rifle."

Steve realized now what had been troubling him. He shoved the bedclothes away, jumped out and began to dress hurriedly.

"Is your rifle in bad shape, Steve?" Bud asked.

"Pretty dusty all over," he acknowledged without looking up from the shoes he was lacing. "There's a lot of rust in the trigger and some pretty bad pits and rust in the bore."

Bud shook his head but said, "Well, if he doesn't keep us out there too long and if we get through chow okay, you'll have time to work on it. Manny and I'll give you a hand with your sack."

In a few minutes the platoon had run through morning roll call and was marching to the parade ground where the exercise was given. There, Sergeant Swifteagle gave a series of commands which extended the platoon over a wide area, each recruit having plenty of space on all sides.

Despite the chill dampness of the morning, Swifteagle ordered the men to shed their dungaree jackets. Then the exercise began. Grasping the $9\frac{1}{2}$-pound rifle in both hands, the recruits used the weapon as if it were a gymnast's bar.

Moving in unison at the big Indian's commands, they raised the Garands over their heads, lowered them to the chests, pushed them straight out, then held them there at arm's length.

It was this position which took the most out of Steve. The weapon's weight seemed to double, then redouble. Swifteagle kept the platoon in that anguishing stance for several minutes before running through another sequence.

But the leadlike rifle and his aching arms didn't keep Steve's mind off the real crisis he faced. Could he get his M-1 ready for the first really searching inspection of boot camp?

This question plagued him all during the seemingly endless prebreakfast exercise. At last, Sergeant Swifteagle halted the exertions, ordered jackets back on, returned the platoon to normal formation and hurried it over to the mess hall.

All Steve wanted to do was to get breakfast over with in a hurry. But as his luck that morning would have it, by the time Platoon 164 reached the chow line, the supply of some of the cooked food ran out. While the cooks back in the galley hurriedly prepared more, the recruits waited impatiently, none more anxious than Steve.

"We're running late this morning, eh, Fletch?" whispered Manny Hernandez, next to him in line.

"I'll say. And just when I needed a lot of extra time to clean up my rifle."

In a few minutes the messmen scurried out with trays of flapjacks and country sausages. The 1st Battalion officer of the day was in the mess hall when the food supply ran out and he watched with a stern eye as the food was served. Mess line breakdowns weren't supposed to occur, in boot camp or any other place in the Marine Corps.

Steve ate quickly and silently, ignoring the noisy banter of the table. As soon as he finished he went outside and took his place in the platoon formation in front of the mess hall. Only the platoon's sentry stood by the silent stacks of rifles.

The unit would not shove off for the hut area until every one of the sixty-one members had finished breakfast. Steve knew this; he also knew that Swifteagle always insisted that each man eat as much as he wanted and take all the time he needed. Ordinarily Steve appreciated this practice. But not this morning.

He waited there, wishing that his impatience could somehow communicate itself to the rest of the platoon.

It seemed an endless vigil but it was probably shorter than

on ordinary mornings when the platoon was not facing a special inspection.

All the routine morning work usually done before chow awaited the platoon when it returned to its two huts—beds to be made, floors swabbed, trash cans emptied, fire extinguishers polished, the head swept and then hosed out and the area adjacent to the huts cleaned of trash and its sand raked neatly. Some of these responsibilities were individual, others were assigned to groups of squad size or smaller "police details."

As Steve hurriedly put the finishing touches on his bunk, he became aware that Billy Joe Dence, his squad leader, had approached and was watching him.

" 'Bout through, Fletcher?" the tall Texan asked.

"Yeah," Steve replied, "but don't you start assigning me any details. We three guys polished fire extinguishers yesterday," he declared, nodding in the direction of his companions, Bud and Manny.

Dence ignored this unsolicited information. "Fourth squad's turn to police the bath hut this morning," he declared blandly. "You three guys turn to it as soon as you're finished making up your racks."

Steve abandoned his bunkmaking and strode after Dence, who was returning to his bunk at the front of the hut. "Dence," he shouted in an angry voice, "get off our backs, will you? It's not our turn for a police detail this morning. Besides, I need the time to work on my rifle."

Dence swung about, confronting Fletcher and his two partners, who had joined him to protest. "Quit the gum beating or I'll run you up to the D.I.," he threatened. "If you're so worried about your rifle, why did you hit the sack last night instead of working on your piece?"

This question was too hot for Steve. Seeing he had his adversary on the defensive, Dence screwed his face into a smirk, leered a moment at Steve and then turned and sauntered back to his bunk.

The three men polished the four brass extinguishers. By

the time they had finished, some members of the platoon were already waiting in formation on the company street, being joined by a steady trickle of recruits from both the platoon's huts.

Steve realized to his intense discomfort that he could do no more than dust off the exterior of his M-1—running his toothbrush down between the gas cylinder and barrel, around the trigger housing and over the butt plate.

He had not finished this when he heard Swifteagle's deep voice, "Platoon 164, on the road."

With an audible sigh, he thrust the brush into a hip pocket, tightened the rifle's sling and without turning to make the usual last-minute inspection of his bunk, he plodded reluctantly outside, wondering what the morning held.

Both Swifteagle and Corporal Bailey were present, the senior instructor counting cadence and giving the commands while the junior man corrected various errors in carriage and stride of the marching men.

Platoon 164 was soon at the parade ground, crowded with its usual activity. Swifteagle guided his unit to a less congested area. As he gave orders which opened space between the squads so that there would be room for the inspection, a large, freckled-faced master sergeant advanced and circled the platoon appraisingly. "Tell them who I am, Sergeant," he gruffly ordered Swifteagle.

The Indian's usually stern visage brightened slightly at this seemingly immodest directive. "Master Sergeant O'Hara, 1st Battalion field sergeant major, will supervise the personnel and rifle inspection," Swifteagle announced.

Through rumor, the reputation of Red Mike O'Hara was known to every recruit a few days after he reached boot camp. A marine for more than 30 of his 48 years, the field sergeant major was a colorful character. His hair, a close-cropped crew cut, was carrot color. His fame derived from his almost irrepressible spirits, his witty, biting tongue and his physical courage which won him decorations for gallantry. He had fought in the "banana wars" of Haiti and Nicaragua, in the Pacific from Guadalcanal to Okinawa and he was serving with the 1st Marine Brigade when it was sent to Korea to repel the Communist invasion.

O'Hara, one of a fast-vanishing breed, had never taken a wife. He was married to the Marine Corps. Expert rifleman, machine gunner, demolitions man, Red Mike was an infantryman's infantryman.

With many misgivings, Steve observed this formidable man looking him over as he stood at attention in the front, hence most exposed, squad.

O'Hara approached Steve slowly, head lowered and eyes squinty in a pose of exaggerated scrutiny. When he was less than a yard away, he reached out and grasped the top button of Steve's dungaree jacket. "Want this?" he asked in a voice dripping with mock sweetness and solicitude.

To his acute discomfort Steve realized that in the pre-inspection haste and confusion, he had forgotten to button his dungaree jacket all the way up, for Marine recruits a serious failure. He tried to think of some answer for the field sergeant major.

"Speak up, Recruit. Do you want this button? Button, button, do you want the button?" Red Mike accented each word with a gentle tug on the button.

"Yes, sir," Steve finally responded meekly.

"Well, here it is!" O'Hara shouted, yanking it off and dropping it into the breast pocket of Steve's jacket.

Both Swifteagle and Bailey were observing the scene. Steve could see that they were not amused. Neither was he.

The sergeant major swaggered down the squad. Steve heard him barking a question or order or comment as he passed along the file.

No time was lost in getting the rifle inspection underway. Corporal Bailey took the 1st squad, Sergeant Swifteagle the

4th. Steve the third tallest man in his squad was so close to the squad leader, Billy Joe Dence, that his eye received only a blurred image of what was taking place.

In a series of briskly executed stepping and facing movements, Sergeant Swifteagle took a position exactly in front of Dence and about a foot away. In the prescribed manner, Dence came to port arms, snapped open the bolt of his rifle, shot a quick glance to see that a round was not in his chamber (a formality for they were not issued ammunition until they got to the rifle range) and then snapped his head back into the position of attention.

But instead of remaining open, the bolt of Dence's rifle slammed shut, catching the fleshy part of his thumb. The Texan swore slightly and would have dropped his rifle had not Swifteagle grabbed it.

Recruits in the vicinity snickered.

Steve did not join them. He was preoccupied with how Swifteagle would react to his own dirty, rusty rifle. What could he say to the D.I.?

After some confusion, Dence managed to present his rifle for inspection. It did not pass. There is a Marine Corps adage which states that no boot's rifle ever passes inspection. Some are merely not as bad as others. Steve could tell from Swifteagle's comments that Dence's rifle wasn't in bad condition.

Next in the squad was Big Jawn Gillyard, the quiet, friendly Negro from Chicago. Except for some dirt on the butt plate, Swifteagle could find no fault with Gillyard's weapon.

As the drill instructor slapped the M-1 back into Big Jawn's hands, he began the movements which would bring him face-to-face with Steve. The recruit felt tension mounting; his abdominal muscles tightened, his breathing came more rapid, his hands trembled.

Steve, almost unseeing, heard the drill instructor's shoes crunch on the abrasive surface of the macadam grinder, and the snappy clicks produced by his heels as he executed a right face and a left face. This was done so briskly that almost before Steve realized it, Swifteagle was staring him up and down, inspecting him from haircut to field shoes.

Steve brought his rifle to port arms and opened the bolt. The Indian deftly slapped it out of his hands and spun it around until its butt was high in the air. Swifteagle held the piece in his right hand by the barrel, its muzzle slightly higher than his right eye.

He peered up the bore, bathed in sunlight which streamed in through the open chamber.

Fletcher waited. Strangely enough, snatches of the Marines' "Rifle Creed" went through his mind. This is my rifle . . . My rifle is my best friend . . . I must master it as I master my life . . . I will ever keep my rifle clean and ready even as I am ready. My rifle and myself are the defenders of my country. . . .

Not since the night his father had called him in and given him the Marines-or-reform-school ultimatum had anxiety gripped him so.

Swifteagle squinted up the M-1's bore for some time. Then he lowered the rifle, blinked a couple of times and again looked at the muzzle. This second inspection lasted only a few seconds. The drill instructor slowly lowered the rifle in a wide arc until the butt rested on the deck.

"This is the foulest, rustiest bore that I've ever seen in a stateside rifle." The Indian's words were formed slowly; he did not raise his voice. "Have you ever cleaned it?"

Steve waited a moment then stammered, "Y . . . yes, sir."

"Not last night you didn't," was the drill instructor's challenge.

To add to his consternation, Steve saw that Field Sergeant Major O'Hara was watching the episode closely.

"Let me see that piece," he demanded, stalking up to them. He took Fletcher's rifle and held it aloft in both hands, as if it were a huge bottle. He looked up the muzzle.

Steve, Swifteagle and the others in the squad observed the

old sergeant. His inspection took little time. He let the rifle drop almost to the deck before catching it by the stock. Turning to Steve, O'Hara stared at him for a full minute before bellowing out, "Cleaner rifles than this sent marines to Portsmouth naval prison to make little rocks out of big ones. That was in the old corps, before World War II. I don't know what a rifle like this'll get you now . . . but I mean to find out right now.

"Sergeant Swifteagle, I'm taking this recruit up to see the man," O'Hara continued, his face getting redder, his voice louder. "I've seen dogfaces with rifles this bad; I've seen swab jockies; I may have seen Coast Guard hooligans. But never in 32 years in the Marine Corps have I ever seen a marine with a piece like this." He shook it, like a dust mop.

"He's yours," Swifteagle stated simply.

Beckoning Steve with a nod, the burly field sergeant major started off across the parade ground. Unmilitarily, Steve broke ranks and followed him. O'Hara clutched the rifle in his hand. The pair headed for 1st Recruit Battalion headquarters, at the opposite corner of the drill field. They were followed by the stares of other platoons whose members and D.I.'s sensed that something unusual was afoot.

Red Mike's stride was long, his pace brisk. Steve had to stretch to keep up with him. Though he had no clear idea of what was going to happen, he assumed that to "see the man" meant going before some officer, possibly even the battalion commander, Lieutenant Colonel Barton. But he couldn't be sure.

Steve puzzled over the fact that neither Swifteagle nor O'Hara had given him a chance to explain why he had not cleaned his rifle. He knew that he had no honest excuse. This bothered him; perhaps more than he was aware.

The two marines, recruit and master sergeant, cleared the parade ground and O'Hara strode across a wide lawn which ran like a green belt between the buildings and the paved expanse. Steve followed.

Still walking briskly, the field sergeant major swung down the colonnaded walk and through the swinging doors that led to battalion headquarters. Only then did Red Mike pause and turn to see if Steve still followed him. The march resumed. Steve wondered more and more where it would end.

They brushed past a Marine private, seated by a small desk at the junction of the entry and a hall. The orderly jumped to attention, knocking over a bugle placed on the table. It fell with a clatter to the tile floor. O'Hara did not even look down.

At the end of the hall loomed a cavernous room, full of desks and filing cabinets. Steve had been here before on early morning cleaning details. But the office looked different now, filled with marines, both male and female, busy with typing and other clerical tasks.

Just before the hall ended, O'Hara swerved into a smaller room. Responding to the gruff order, "Wait outside," Steve took a position of attention near the door. He looked up at the sign, "Adjutant," in bold, gold letters on a crimson background over the door.

He heard O'Hara say to someone in the office, "Morning, Gunner, I got a hot one. Is the colonel in?"

Steve's spirits sagged. He had hoped that somehow his case could remain out of official channels and be settled informally. But the field sergeant major was preparing to take it straight to Lieutenant Colonel Barton, the battalion C.O. Steve wanted to rush into the adjutant's office and try to plead for a delay. But fear and confusion locked his feet and tongue.

"Yeah, Red Mike, Colonel Barton's in," the adjutant responded. "But he's heading up to depot headquarters in a couple of minutes to see the G-3. What's got you so hot to trot?"

Steve held his breath, hoping that O'Hara would be dissuaded from forcing the meeting with Lieutenant Colonel Barton. O'Hara's reply dashed this dream.

"See this rifle?" he roared. "It's the foulest piece I've ever seen in the hands of a live marine. I've got the recruit out in the passageway. I want to take him and his dirty rifle in to see the colonel now, while the evidence is hot."

"Is it really that bad?" the adjutant asked.

"It's worse," O'Hara speedily reassured him.

"Well, if the field sergeant major wants to see the battalion commander on a matter he considers urgent, there's nothing for the adjutant to do but set up the interview. Stand by a minute, Mike."

Steve stiffened up as the adjutant came out of his office and crossed the corridor to a door under the sign "Battalion Commander." As he knocked, the adjutant turned and inspected Steve. Before the scrutiny became uncomfortable, a voice from within sounded, "Come in."

The adjutant opened and entered. He stood at attention with the door ajar. Steve did not have to strain to hear what was being said.

"The field sergeant major wants to have the colonel see what he says is the worst rifle he's ever seen a live marine own. He's got the owner along, too."

Steve heard a deeper voice slowly answer, "Well, Gunner, I am due up at Colonel Wellborn's office at 0930. That gives Red Mike only a few minutes. But tell him to bring his recruit along in. He must have something. He doesn't push the panic button on minor matters."

The adjutant stepped out into the hall without closing the door to the battalion commander's office. Steve could tell by the creaking of the floorboards and the great shadow projected into the corridor that Red Mike had walked to the adjutant's doorway and was standing there, awaiting the decision.

"The colonel will see you and the recruit, Sergeant Major," the adjutant answered. "He hasn't much time so better make it brief."

"Brief as I can," was O'Hara's uncompromising response.

Turning to Steve, he ordered, "March in there, take a position directly in front of the colonel's desk and about a pace away. Keep your cover in your right hand and stand at attention."

Steve was slow in understanding. He stood, eying O'Hara questioningly.

"Move out, move," the N.C.O. barked, helping Steve to a stumbling start with a tug on the elbow. Still at a loss as to the proper thing to do, Steve proceeded cautiously into Lieutenant Colonel Barton's office, approached his desk and stood at attention. The field sergeant major took up a position at a corner of the desk, somewhat closer to the officer.

The colonel was the first to speak. "Sorry I lighted this up," he said with a slight smile, brandishing a large cigar, "but I was just about to take off for headquarters and I was going to smoke this en route. A little *cigar* smoke won't bother you, will it, Sergeant Major? Not after all the smoke of battle you've swallowed, eh?"

The officer's friendly manner made Steve breathe a little more easily. When he was standing on the platform in the barnlike training shed giving his welcoming address, the battalion commander seemed remote, severe—an unfeeling fighting machine. Now the impression was different.

Steve was so close he could see the thinning hair on Barton's Prussian-cropped head, his cold, blue eyes, the large Marine Corps ring he wore on the little finger of his left hand. His four rows of campaign ribbons and decorations made a vivid splash of color. From the chart of U.S. military ribbons which hung on the wall of his quonset hut, Steve could identify the ribbon centered above all the others on Barton's chest as the Congressional Medal of Honor, the nation's highest award for heroism.

Fletcher noticed also that Lieutenant Colonel Barton had won the Silver Star and that he had the Purple Heart with two gold stars, signifying that he had been wounded in action three times. The only other one he could recognize was on the far right in the lowest row, the Korean Citation ribbon, blue and white, the colors of the Republic of Korea's flag.

It was quite thrilling to be close to an authentic hero. The room itself had an easing atmosphere. Without being luxurious, it was comfortable. A dark-green rug covered the floor and the single window was hung with draperies of the same green hue. Lieutenant Colonel Barton's highly polished mahogany desk was clean except for an ash tray and a two-tiered tray, one section labeled "In," the other "Out."

Behind his chair were two flags, planted in bright, brass floor stands. One was Old Glory, the other was the crimson and gold standard of the United States Marine Corps. A large bookcase covered almost all of one wall; on the other three were maps, pictures, documents and a pair of crossed swords.

The battalion commander drew deeply on his cigar, leaned forward in his chair and knocked the ash from the glowing tip. Exhaling a tight jet of smoke toward the ceiling, he looked at the sergeant major and said, "The adjutant says that you found a pretty dirty rifle this morning."

"Never seen a live marine with a worse one, any time, any place!" O'Hara reported emphatically.

"What's your name, Lad?" Lieutenant Colonel Barton asked, staring straight at Steve.

"Private Stephen Fletcher, sir."

"Let me see that rifle, Sergeant Major," the battalion commander ordered, rising from his chair and walking around to the front of the desk. O'Hara handed the M-1 to the officer butt-first.

Lieutenant Colonel Barton walked over to the window slowly. Steve noticed that as he was doing this, he inserted a shiny barrel reflector into the rifle's chamber. The officer exposed this part of the weapon to the sun's rays filtering in the window. It dawned on Steve that the instrument was some sort of optical device to catch light and "bend" it, similar to a periscope, so that it shone down the rifle's bore.

Out of the corner of his eye, Steve watched the battalion commander squint down the muzzle, revolving the weapon slightly to capture more light. The officer spent more than a minute gazing into the rifle. Then he withdrew the instrument and popped it into his pocket. For another minute or so he inspected other parts of the rifle—opening and closing the bolt, testing the trigger action, running his fingers over the sights.

During this inspection, the battalion commander said nothing. The only sound in the room was Red Mike O'Hara's agitated breathing. Finally Barton returned to his desk, putting the Garand across the top. He sat down in his chair, picked up his telephone and dialed.

The room was so quiet that Steve could hear the dial tone buzz off and on. A voice answered on the other end of the line.

"This is Lieutenant Colonel Barton down in the 1st Recruit Training Battalion. I'd like to be put through to Colonel Wellborn."

A few moments passed before another voice was heard. The battalion commander stated his case. "Colonel, sir, this is Lieutenant Colonel Barton. I'd like to postpone that appointment I have with you; something's come up down here at the battalion which I'd like to handle right away."

Steve's heart jumped. He had never believed before this that fright could cause one's knees to knock together. Now he knew better. His own were slapping together uncontrollably.

The request granted, Barton concluded his phone conversation. Grinding out his cigar he looked at Steve and said, "Stand at ease, Fletcher. This is going to take some time."

Steve broadened his stance and relaxed a bit.

"What platoon are you in?" the battalion commander asked.

"The 164th, sir."

"That's Sergeant Swifteagle's," Barton responded. "You're in your third week of training."

"That's right, sir," O'Hara interposed. "He turned up with this rifle at the third week inspection."

Barton spun his chair and flipped up a switch of an inter-com box behind his desk; the speaker hummed, then grew silent. He leaned over near the speaker. "First Sergeant, First Sergeant."

Almost immediately there came a "Yes, sir."

"Top, bring me in the record book of Pvt. Stephen Fletcher, Platoon 164."

"Aye, aye, sir," was the acknowledgment.

The battalion commander snapped the switch off and swung around. "Sergeant Major, for you the smoking lamp is lit. Light up if you want."

Before Red Mike could light a cigarette, there was a knock on the door.

The first sergeant entered and placed a large, cardboard folder on the desk, about-faced neatly and departed. Lieu-tenant Colonel Barton opened the book and flipped through the pages, stopping frequently to examine entries.

"Fletcher," he said after he had gone through the folder and slapped it shut, "there's nothing in here to explain why you have made such a poor showing. You have a better than average I.Q.; finished high school; you come from a good home; your father's a professional man, a lawyer. You're the stuff good marines are made out of.

"What's your story? Explain this to me," Barton said, rap-ping on the stock of the rifle with his knuckles.

Steve paused a moment, trying desperately to think of some excuse. The officer's remarks reminded him of talkings-to given him by the high school principal and the football coach back home. Now as then, Steve was at a loss to explain.

"Speak up, Lad," Barton urged impatiently. "Don't you have anything to say for yourself? How is it you came to a rifle inspection with your weapon in this condition? How is it that you ever allowed it to get this bad in the first place?"

"Sir," Steve stammered, "I don't know."

"Don't know?" the officer exploded. "Why of course you know. What did you do last night during free time?"

"I went to sleep, sir," Steve admitted in a slow, subdued voice.

"Went to sleep?" Barton inquired incredulously. "While the rest of the platoon got ready for the inspection?"

"Yes, sir," Steve confessed.

"That beats anything I've ever heard," Red Mike O'Hara interjected.

"Were you sick from inoculation shots or something?" Barton queried, trying to get to the bottom of an episode which obviously puzzled him.

"No, sir, but I was tired," Steve added hopefully, using the only excuse he could make.

"Tired! Why marines are always tired! You can bet your life that there were about 18,000 bone-tired marines over in Korea with the 1st Marine Division. Tired, cold and scared. But they were combat-ready. With a rifle that rusty and dirty, you are not combat-ready."

There was a pause; Steve attempted to form some words. What he really wanted, though, was to get the interview over with and return to his platoon.

"You know the Marines' 'Rifle Creed,' don't you?" Barton asked.

"I do, sir," Steve confessed. "Sergeant Swifteagle made us memorize it."

Lieutenant Colonel Barton stood up, grabbed Steve's M-1 and came around the desk with it. "That creed was written by the late Gen. William Rupertus. He commanded the 1st Marine Division when it invaded Peleliu in the Pacific; there was no fiercer fighting in World War II or any war. On D-Day the temperature was over 100° and the Navy doctors advised the general to postpone the invasion, saying it was too hot to fight.

"However, General Rupertus knew that the grand strategy
of the war required that the timetable be kept. The support-
ing ships and aircraft would soon be needed elsewhere. The
marines hit the beach at the scheduled H-Hour."

The battalion commander handed Steve back his rifle. "I
tell you this because you said that you were too tired to clean
your rifle. Well," and he paused here for a moment, "it wasn't
too hot for those marines to fight and die. They weren't too
tired to do their job. And a whole lot of them weren't as big,
as strong, or as smart as you are. And many were younger
than you.

"I also tell you that story because during the first part of
World War II, General Rupertus commanded this very base.
In fact, he wrote the 'Rifle Creed' right up in that office."
The battalion commander drew the recruit over to the win-
dow and pointed up the parade ground to the headquarters
building.

"So when I see this rifle of yours and try to figure out a just
punishment—just for you and for the Marine Corps—I have
to think of General Rupertus and ask myself, 'What would
he do?'

"And there's only one answer: court-martial.

"Field Sergeant Major, take this man back to his platoon.
Tell Sergeant Swifteagle that I've awarded Private Fletcher
a summary court-martial and that he will continue training
with his platoon until the court meets."

"What about his rifle, Colonel? Should it be kept as evidence?"

"Good idea, Mike. I'll have the battalion legal officer keep
it in his custody."

"Aye, aye, sir. Fletcher, let's move out. You've taken enough
of the colonel's time and mine this morning." With that
O'Hara swung open the door and pointed out to the passageway.

Steve Fletcher trod slowly out of the office, his mind racing
with thoughts. From the lectures on military justice he'd

heard during the first 2 weeks of boot camp, he knew that a summary court-martial could sentence him to the brig, fine him, give him a bad conduct discharge. Ruin him for life. At best, his Marine Corps career appeared spoiled before it had much more than started.

I made a mistake, Steve mused bitterly. I should have gone to reform school and gotten it over with.

Chapter 10

LIEUTENANT COLONEL BARTON DECIDES

NOT a word passed between Red Mike O'Hara and Steve during the long walk from battalion headquarters to the hut area.

As they neared 164's quonsets, Steve perceived that the rifle and personnel inspection had been completed. Recruits hurried in and out of the two huts. Sergeant Swifteagle and Corporal Bailey stood in the middle of the company street, observing their men and talking. They looked up inquiringly at the approaching pair. The field sergeant major was the first to speak.

"You can have your foul-up back," Red Mike informed them.

"What did he get?" Swifteagle asked.

"The old man gave him a summary court."

"You took him to see *Colonel Barton?*" Bailey inquired incredulously.

"When I take a recruit to see the man, I take him to see the man," O'Hara rejoined emphatically.

"He stays with the platoon?" the senior drill instructor asked.

"Yeah," O'Hara answered, "it's only when a man is awaiting a general court-martial that he goes to the brig. That place is crowded to the overheads; and this way a recruit keeps up with his training until the trial. But Fletcher will need a new rifle. We're keeping the old one as evidence."

With that, O'Hara turned and strutted back up the company street. Steve watched him disappear, wishing fervently that he had never known the "old salt" except by reputation.

"Fletcher, you'll have to wait until later to pick up a new rifle. We're falling out in a couple of minutes for a training film and lecture." Swifteagle's words broke into Steve's bitter reflections.

"Yes, sir," he mumbled and made off for his hut.

The usual tumult and shouting subsided as soon as Steve entered the door. Billy Joe Dence, who was nearest the door, was the first to rush up. "Where did Red Mike take you? Are you in a jam?" He was almost grinning and an eager tone animated his voice.

Steve pushed the Texan aside and jostled his way through the circle of questioning recruits to his bunk. Only his two pals, Bud Ajamian and Manny Hernandez, refrained from joining the curious throng. They waited for him at his bunk.

Bud was the first to speak, "What happened, Steve? Make out okay?"

"O'Hara took me to see Colonel Barton," Steve announced in a low tone.

"Colonel Barton!" they both gasped simultaneously.

Manny was the first to speak up, "Did he inspect your rifle?"

"He sure did. With a microscope or something."

"What did you get out of it?" Bud asked, a worried expression furrowing his face.

"A summary court-martial," Steve responded gravely.

"A summary court-martial!" Bud repeated, almost in disbelief. "That's rough, Steve. I hate to say this but you shouldn't have taken that chance last night," he blurted out, more in sorrow than condemnation.

Soon the drill instructors sounded another call to assembly and the hut was cleared of recruits. Latecomers already were being berated by the time the three buddies ran out of the hut and fell into ranks. The platoon marched off for another phase of its concentrated training schedule.

It was impossible for Steve to keep secret the news of his court-martial. When Billy Joe Dence heard, he was highly amused. "You'll probably go to the brig for life, maybe even the firing squad," he joked.

But the rest of the men, particularly Bud and Manny, tried to encourage Steve and help keep his spirits up as he plodded through the long, hard days with an added ordeal confronting him.

He needed their support. The regimentation of military life, the close-order drill which was both a physical and emotional trial, the classroom lectures and field demonstrations, the early morning calisthenics, the innumerable little chores and the increasing pressure which accompanied all these activities made boot camp more and more irksome.

Remembering that he had completed less than 3 of the 10-week training stint caused Steve's spirits to droop even lower. I don't think I can stick it out, he told himself.

His suspense over the trial was ended 4 days after his visit to Lieutenant Colonel Barton's office. After marching the platoon back from morning chow that day, Sergeant Swifteagle called Steve aside. "Soon as you get your bunk squared away, report to Lieutenant Zanutto in the S-3 office at battalion headquarters," the D.I. ordered.

Steve looked inquiringly at the D.I. but his broad features wore their usual expression of inscrutability. "We'll be in Training Shed 8 until 0930; if you get back after that, report to the 'Gas Chamber,' " Swifteagle instructed.

Though the drill instructor gave him no hint about the purpose of the call Steve was not surprised, upon presenting himself to Lieutenant Zanutto at the battalion training office, that it involved his court-martial.

"Fletcher, you're to be tried by special court tomorrow at 0900," Zanutto informed him. "The battalion commander has appointed me your defense counsel. Tell me your story."

Steve explained as best he could the background of the episode; that he had been tired and gone to sleep early thinking that he could clean his rifle in the morning before breakfast, that the time he had expected to be free was consumed by an unexpected physical drill and by delays in the mess hall.

Zanutto commented, "There's not much of a defense but I recommend that you plead not guilty tomorrow. I'll do my best to present your case."

He handed Steve a copy of the charge sheet and then told him to return to his platoon.

Steve did so. He located his mates at Training Shed 8, listening to a lecture about chemical warfare—poison gases, their properties and effects and how to recognize them by their odor.

At 0830 the next morning a military policeman armed with a .45 and wearing his MP brassard appeared at the hut to march Steve to the court, an office room in battalion headquarters. Three officers, a major flanked by a pair of captains, sat behind a long table. There were three smaller tables, one occupied by Lieutenant Zanutto, the second by another lieutenant. A woman Marine staff sergeant sat at the third desk, ready with notebook and row of sharpened pencils.

Lieutenant Zanutto beckoned to Steve to join him at his table. When he was seated Steve noticed that there was a rifle on the floor beside the desk of the other lieutenant. "Is that mine?" he asked his defense counsel. Lieutenant Zanutto nodded his head affirmatively and whispered, "He's the prosecutor."

Promptly at 0900 the court-martial began. As Steve suspected, the three officers behind the long table were the judges and the woman marine the court reporter.

Various participants in the proceedings were sworn. The prosecutor read the charges aloud and the senior judge asked Steve to plead.

"Not guilty," Fletcher replied firmly.

Quite briskly, the prosecutor entered the rifle as evidence and then presented Field Sergeant Major O'Hara as a witness for the prosecution. Red Mike made a forceful, effective witness. He was cross-examined by Lieutenant Zanutto and queried by all three judges, who carefully examined the rifle. Then Sergeant Swifteagle appeared in the court and testified.

The evidence and the testimony seemed more damaging to Steve than the previous episode in Lieutenant Colonel Barton's office. This defeatist attitude reflected itself when Steve was called upon to testify in his own behalf. He faltered badly.

Both prosecution and defense made their final pleas; in less than an hour, the swiftly moving trial was concluded and the courtroom cleared for the judges' secret deliberations. Closely watched by the guard, Steve waited outside the building. After about 20 minutes one of the captains stuck his head out of the door and announced, "Court is reconvened. Bring in the prisoner."

When all had filed back into the room, the major ordered, "The accused will come forward."

Lieutenant Zanutto directed Steve to a spot in front of the judges' table.

He walked there and stood at attention, his knees again knocking, his mind filled with fear. When all had been seated, the major stood and slowly read, "We find the accused, Pvt. Stephen Fletcher of Platoon 164, 1st Recruit Training Battalion, Marine Corps Recruit Depot, San Diego, California, guilty as charged and sentence him to pay a fine of 93 dollars, in three monthly installments and to be confined in the depot brig 15 days on reduced rations, with full rations every third day. Court is adjourned."

Steve stood helpless on the spot, not knowing what to do next. Lieutenant Zanutto walked over to him and shook his hand. "Did the best I could, Fletcher, but you didn't give me much to work with. It was a pretty fair sentence, but you won't enjoy that 15 days on bread and water."

"Is that what the major meant by 'reduced rations'?" Steve asked.

"That's right," the lieutenant replied.

"How did they decide on that 93 dollars for the fine?" the recruit asked.

"That's what an M-1 rifle costs the taxpayers," Zanutto explained. "Usual way to compute a fine for your type of offense."

"Sir," the guard announced to Lieutenant Zanutto, "I had orders to return Fletcher to battalion headquarters if the court found him guilty."

"Right," the defense counsel agreed. Turning to Steve he said, "The colonel will decide whether to confine you now, before he reads the trial record and approves your sentence."

Noticing that Steve's face darkened, the lieutenant added, "I don't think that he'll brig you right away."

With a wave of his hand, Zanutto disappeared, walking in the direction of the schooling sheds where his regular battalion S-3 duties—training and operations—took him.

Followed closely by his guard, Steve Fletcher marched toward battalion headquarters, by no means sharing the lieutenant's confidence that he would stay clear of the brig that day.

Under the guard's guidance, Steve reported to the adjutant's office where the sentinel turned in a slip of paper bearing the verdict and sentence, authenticated by the senior member of the court-martial. The adjutant took it immediately into Lieutenant Colonel Barton's office.

Steve waited, facing the adjutant's desk at stiff attention. Unable to observe when the latter would reappear from the battalion commander's office, Fletcher listened intently. Soon he heard Barton's door open and shut and someone cross the hall and enter the room.

It was the adjutant. "Sentry," he ordered briskly, "you can secure."

Without saying anything to Steve, the adjutant circled the

desk and dropped into his chair. The recruit watched him slip a form into his typewriter and hurriedly fill it out.

"Here," he said when he had finished. Without lifting his gaze he ripped the form out of the machine and handed it to Steve. "Take this back to your senior drill instructor."

"Am I free, sir?" Steve cautiously inquired.

"You will continue training until the colonel has had a chance to review your sentence," the adjutant snapped.

Leaving well enough alone, Steve took one step to the rear, about-faced as gracefully as he knew how and hurriedly retreated.

Sergeant Swifteagle had told Steve that the platoon would spend the morning at the gas chamber, learning the use of the gas mask. He reached there in time to join the 4th squad and enter the chamber, clouded with tear gas. They had to sing all the stanzas of "The Marines' Hymn" before being allowed to slip the gas mask over tear-drenched cheeks and rush with shouts of relief from the noxious compartment.

After noon chow, there was a long session of close-order drill. The two D.I.'s marched the platoon up and down the lengthy parade ground—commanding, correcting; commanding, correcting; commanding, correcting. Platoon 164 was gradually becoming a polished marching unit. The improvement apparent that afternoon amazed Steve. Only 3 weeks before, the recruits stumbled into one another, dropped rifles and responded unsurely to commands.

When a drill instructor barked an order that afternoon, the platoon responded as a unit—feet struck the macadam grinder in unison, rifles moved from one position to another as if activated by a single force.

That afternoon Steve noticed another platoon watching 164 go through its maneuvers—the first time there had been such flattering scrutiny. Their untanned faces, unstained field shoes and wrinkled dungarees betrayed the observers as "new boots."

Steve stifled a surge of pride. After all, he reasoned, I won't be with *this* outfit much longer.

Early that evening Bailey held mail call in the company street. As usual, Steve had a letter from home. His mother wrote almost every day and even his father had written him a couple of times. So had his brother Roger.

Steve himself had not been a faithful correspondent but the drill instructors made everyone write home twice a week, Sunday afternoon and Wednesday night. He had written nothing in these letters that disclosed his personal crisis. He knew that he would have to when transferred from the platoon. But he decided not to mention the trouble he had gotten in until the change of address to the brig made it a harsh reality.

He was well aware how his father would react to the news!

As Steve sat on the edge of his bunk reading the letter from his mother, Bud Ajamian and Manny Hernandez seated themselves beside him. This was the first real chance they had to talk since the court-martial; their faces reflected the questions they had on their minds.

"I've had it," Steve announced, looking up from his letter.

"Brig time?" Manny asked anxiously.

"Brig time," was his laconic answer.

"My aching back," Bud said slowly. "How much?"

"Fifteen days," Steve stated. After that had sunk in on his listeners he added, "Bread and water."

By that time, most of the men in the hut were gathering in a ring around Steve and Bud's bunk. Billy Joe Dence inquired, "How did you make out?"

"How do you think?" Manny responded, his voice thick with sarcasm. "He got a meritorious promotion to master gunnery sergeant. Let's break it up," he added, pushing his way through the crowd to signal that the questioning was over.

It took an instant or two before Dence realized that his leg was being pulled. "Hey, wait a minute," he protested in a thick, angry voice, "that doesn't figure."

"Beat it, Big Boy," Bud Ajamian snarled. "If you knew anything about the Marine Corps, you'd know that when a buddy's in trouble, you help him, not heckle him."

With that the crowd thinned and Dence walked away without a word. No more was said about the subject to Steve that night.

All that next morning was spent at a lecture featuring training films and sand table demonstrations of amphibious attacks. Though he was burdened with worry, Steve enjoyed this class.

When it was over, he had some idea of the immense complexity of an amphibious landing and how the Marine Corps was able to land tens of thousands of men on fiercely defended shores and supply them with food, water, ammunition and medical care. He also began to realize how tank, artillery and air support were co-ordinated and how communications were set up to meet the demands of modern land warfare.

Painstaking planning and organization and tight teamwork, Steve realized, were the qualities which made the impossible possible.

Though he more or less expected to be called to Lieutenant Colonel Barton's office early that day, it passed without incident. So did the second day. Steve's suspense built up hourly.

During the middle of the afternoon of the third day following the court-martial, the platoon was learning how to tear down and reassemble the Browning automatic rifle. The recruits worked at benches in an open area, the special instructor lecturing and demonstrating from a raised platform.

Steve happened to look up and he saw the battalion runner —the same private who sat in the hall near Lieutenant Colonel Barton's office—approaching. The runner went up to the instructor and handed him a piece of paper.

Steve had a premonition that it was a message concerning him, but many previous misgivings had proved false. The instructor signed a receipt for the message, then unfolded and read it. Steve eyed him curiously.

The instructor looked up and called out, "Sergeant Swifteagle and Private Fletcher, report to battalion headquarters immediately."

The big Indian acknowledged the order with a clipped, "Roger," and then called over to Steve, "Fletcher, fall out."

Steve threaded his way out of the crowded instruction compound. "We'll swing past your hut on our way so you can pick up your toilet gear. If the old man is going to send you to the brig today, you won't have to go back to the hut." Not knowing exactly how to react to this thoughtful thoroughness, Steve set out with Swifteagle, matching him stride for giant stride.

Their rapid pace under Southern California's hot November sun brought the perspiration oozing from Steve's forehead. Within a few minutes they reached the quonset hut.

While the drill instructor waited at the door, Steve ducked in and went to his footlocker. The hut's interior was dark and cool, and for the first time Steve realized how comfortable it was. He looked up at Bud Ajamian's bunk, made in its usual faultless fashion. Steve knew that he would miss Bud and Manny and the other regular guys in the squad and platoon.

The door at the other end of the hut swung open suddenly and the shaft of sunlight blurred Steve's vision. It was the platoon sentry, walking a post manned 24 hours a day in the platoon area by recruits chosen alphabetically for 2-hour tours of duty.

"What're you doing?" the guard inquired.

Steve was filling his canvas ditty bag with soap, washcloth, toothbrush and powder. "I'm getting ready to go to the brig," Steve replied after an embarrassed pause.

The guard stepped closer and peered down at Steve, blinking his eyes to adjust them to the diminished light. "Oh, it's you, Fletcher," he concluded knowingly.

At this point Swifteagle looked in and said, "That's all right, Sentry. Fletcher's with me. He's getting some gear out of his locker box. Hurry it up, Fletcher."

Steve had the toilet articles he wanted. He slammed down the lid of his locker box, secured it and then pushed it back into place underneath his bunk.

The incident with the inquisitive guard chilled some of his nostalgia at leaving the platoon. Why did that guy have to come poking around? Steve thought bitterly. That's the Marine Corps for you. Someone's always snooping around making sure that everything's going perfect. These Sneaky Petes get me down. He sighed disgustedly.

When they entered battalion headquarters, Swifteagle and Steve reported to the adjutant's office. As soon as they appeared in the doorway, the adjutant waved them on. "Right into the colonel's office. Go ahead; he's waiting for you."

The two turned and crossed the passageway. The drill instructor knocked on the door. "Come in," was the prompt response. When Swifteagle opened the door, Steve was surprised to see that the colonel had another visitor, Red Mike O'Hara. He wondered what this signified.

According to protocol, which he was learning rapidly, Steve strode to a spot centered in front of Lieutenant Colonel Barton's desk and snapped to attention. Swifteagle took a similar stance at the recruit's left.

The colonel looked them both over closely for a minute or so. His inspection completed, he said, "At ease."

With a grim face and stern eyes, he looked straight at Steve. "Know why you're here?"

"Yes, sir," Steve replied.

"Why?" the commander queried.

"The sentence of my court-martial doesn't become effective until the colonel approves it. I assume that has been completed and I'm here to be told that I'm going to the brig."

Lieutenant Colonel Barton nodded, and a slight smile flitted over his face. "In essence you are correct. But such experiences as these can teach more if accompanied by an explanation."

Steve's heart sank. Not only was he going to the brig but he would have to listen to a long, fatherly-type speech.

"Fletcher, I've been commanding here for 6 months. That's not a long time as tours of duty go but I've had a chance to see a lot of marines pass through the 1st Recruit Training Battalion. How many would you say, Sergeant Major?"

"Roughly about 2,500, sir," Red Mike stated.

"About 2,500. That's a lot of recruits. I bring this figure up, Fletcher, because I want to say that none of the recruit discipline cases brought up before me has troubled me more than yours."

Steve revealed obvious surprise at this statement.

"Puzzled, huh?" the battalion commander observed. "Well let me explain. In almost every one of those other cases I could sense some basic personal problem, some strong influence working on an essentially weak or unintelligent person. Now, I don't intend to drift off into sociological jargon but I think you can follow me.

"Fletcher, when I study your background I see nothing to explain your conduct. I see a strong, healthy, intelligent young man, born in one of the finest regions of America. But in you I see a young man who does not want to take advantage of any new ideas. It doesn't figure.

"This base exists for one purpose: to make good marines out of good Americans. I think that you're a good American. I'm not at all sure that I'd be fulfilling the mission of this command if I sent you to the brig."

For a moment, Steve couldn't make sense out of this sudden shift. Then his hopes began to rise.

The battalion commander turned to O'Hara. "Sergeant

Major, do you think I'd be letting you down if I suspended Fletcher's brig time?"

Steve turned to watch the expression on Red Mike's face as the old noncom slowly formed his sentences. "Well, sir, 15 years ago I'd of said that the brig was the place for this lad. Now I'm not so sure. Since things in the corps have softened . . ." The sergeant major stopped, seeing an amused smile break out on Lieutenant Colonel Barton's face. "But they *have* softened, Colonel; this isn't the old corps!" O'Hara protested.

The battalion head nodded but he continued to smile.

"I'll come to the point," Red Mike said, quickening his speech. "I've seen men since World War II take a big turn for the better after getting that second chance they'd never had in the old corps. This recruit may have the stuff to be a real 'outgoing' marine. He didn't try to lie out of it. Come to think about it, he didn't whimper. Yes, I think that he could straighten up and fly right—if he sets his mind to it."

All three of the men looked at Steve. He stood there, the center of scrutiny, not knowing what to do.

Lieutenant Colonel Barton broke the ice. "How do you feel about it, Swifteagle?"

"Fletcher could be a good marine, not great, but good. I think he's worth a try."

"Good," the battalion commander declared. Turning his attention to Steve again he said, "Fletcher, I'm suspending your sentence, suspending, not vacating it. One more foul-up and you'll get it back plus anything new that's coming to you.

"Come over here. I want to explain your Service Record Book to you." He motioned for Steve to come around behind his desk.

When Steve got there the officer opened up the book. "Up in heaven they say that the Recording Angel keeps a detailed record of our lives. Well, this S.R.B. is the Marine Corps version of that book. It tells when you enlisted and where you're stationed. If you go on leave, it gets entered here. It will record your transfers, your promotions, your marriage, even what you fired on the rifle range. It also has a page which good marines work hard to keep blank—page 13—a record of punishment. Your's already has one entry.

"Here are two more S.R.B. pages, important to understand and remember. One is used to record your military proficiency, the other to record your personal conduct. A mark of 5 equals 100 per cent. High marks come hard but drop easily —though all recruits usually finish boot camp with the same markings on these pages, 5 and 5."

Lieutenant Colonel Barton tapped the blank pages of Steve's S.R.B. "Fletcher," he intoned in a stern voice, "if you prove the decision I made here today was wrong, I'll not only throw the book at you in a court-martial, I also will give you such low markings here that you'll never be able to bring them up to a respectable level. Got it?"

"Yes, sir . . . and thank . . ."

The battalion commander interrupted curtly, "Don't thank me . . . stand by for a ram if you ever get fouled up again. Now shove off. If I had to spend as much time with the other 900 recruits in this battalion as I have with you, we'd never outpost a finished platoon."

With that, Swifteagle and O'Hara started for the door. Steve followed, not feeling exactly jubilant but mighty relieved.

As he and Swifteagle walked toward the quonset-hut area, Steve spoke up, "Sir, Private Fletcher requests permission to speak to the drill instructor."

"What do you want?" Swifteagle asked gruffly.

"Sir, what did the field sergeant major mean when he said he thought that I could become an outgoing marine?"

"Artillery term. Fire from the enemy is incoming. That's bad. Fire from us going toward enemy is outgoing. That's good. Outgoing marine means the same as hard-charging, gung-ho marine, a good marine."

Though Steve had suspected that this was what Red Mike

O'Hara had meant, the confirming words of Swifteagle's translation were nice.

He did not look forward to 6 more weeks of boot camp; any slip would be disastrous for him. But it was good to know that a tough old veteran thought well of him. It was also good to have a battalion commander like Barton, tough, impossible to bluff or fool, but fair enough to give a man a second chance.

Chapter 11

A FIGHT AND A MARCH

STEVE, you've got to get with it." It was the morning after Steve's reprieve and he listened to Bud Ajamian as they made the two-tiered bunk. They had become deft at this task and worked swiftly, Steve on one side, Bud on the other.

"Sure, you didn't come into the Marine Corps because you wanted to," his buddy continued, "but there are a lot of guys in this platoon who'd rather be back home, too. They're smart enough though to know that you can't beat the system and most of them, maybe all of them, are beginning to love the corps and trying to be good marines."

"I know, Bud," Steve rejoined, "but I had my taste of Marine discipline at home, long before I came here. Ever since the first day of boot camp I've been behind the eight ball for one reason or another. I can't win for losing."

"You are going to try to keep out of any more trouble, aren't you?" Bud inquired seriously.

" 'Course. I'd be a fool not to. But don't expect me to break my back trying to be the all-American marine. I just don't go for the outfit that much. It's too chicken for me. I like things the Army way, more relaxed, casuallike. They do a pretty good job without all this heckling the troops."

"Sure the Army does a pretty good job. But the corps is out to do a great job—the best. That's the difference," Bud retorted.

127

"That's where me and the corps differ. Pretty good is good enough for me," Steve rebutted. "Life's too short."

By this time Bud's bunk was finished and the team shifted its efforts to Steve's, the lower one. The time approached for morning chow. This fact and the stooped position from which they worked seemed to end the conversation.

From the high point when Lieutenant Colonel Barton suspended his brig sentence, Steve's spirits had sagged badly. He pondered his situation a long time in bed that night. As he saw it, every Marine recruit has two strikes on him as soon as he arrives at boot camp. He had these two plus a broken bat!

Steve figured that he could probably make it. However, Lieutenant Colonel Barton's generous gesture hadn't altered his basic discontent with boot camp, or with the entire Marine Corps. It wasn't that it was too rough. Except for Corporal Gurdall's drunken expedition, no one had pushed the platoon around. It was just that the standards were impossibly high—from the way beds should be made to the way to address officers and noncoms.

The Marine Corps spent too much time spinning its wheels, too much time on "busy work." That was what fired his smoldering resentment.

Platoon 164 was in its fourth week of training. At the end of the week recruits would begin a week of mess duty either at the main base or at rifle range. Then came 3 weeks of weapons training at the rifle range. Boot camp scuttlebutt had it that mess duty at the rifle range galley was a better deal than at mainside. So the men of Platoon 164 cheered when Sergeant Swifteagle announced that they would make the 13-mile hike to Camp Matthews, the rifle range, on the approaching Saturday to pull mess duty there.

Before the platoon left for the range, however, its calm and cohesion were momentarily ruptured by an ugly episode.

Early Friday morning Billy Joe Dence was showering in

the bathhouse when Manny Hernandez stepped into the steam-filled room. "Outside, vamoose," the Texan snarled. "Wait till I'm finished."

In the previous weeks of boot camp Dence had partially concealed his anti-Mexican bias. For some inexplicable reason he chose that morning to bare his venomous attitude.

This was not the first time that Manny Hernandez had been exposed to such hatred, such prejudice. He responded to it as he always had—paid no attention to it whatsoever. He continued into the shower.

His quiet defiance outraged Dence. He stepped toward the Gila Bend lad and shoved him back. Manny lost his footing on the shower's wet, soapy floor. He fell, giving himself a nasty smack on the back of the head.

When his senses cleared, he jumped up and started throwing punches at Dence. Despite the fact that the Texan was half a head taller and 30 pounds heavier, the fusillade forced him to retreat. The slick floor made it difficult for Manny to get a foothold to throw any punishing blows. But he headed Dence for a relatively dry corner. Before the pummeling began, a half dozen recruits, attracted to the shower by the noise, separated the two.

Perhaps nothing official would have come of the situation if an alert sentry, attracted by the shouts of the combatants and peacemakers, hadn't rushed into the head. He reported the incident to the drill instructors.

The platoon, especially the 4th squad which had seen at firsthand how the Texan squad leader harassed Manny—always making sure that he had to perform the dirty jobs—anxiously awaited the official reaction.

It was quick in coming. That afternoon the platoon was hearing a lecture on map reading and use of the compass, preparatory to the march to Camp Matthews the next day. The recruits were seated in steep bleachers, shielded from the sun by a sloping roof. A special instructor lectured from the pit of the amphitheater, assisted by Swifteagle and Bailey with charts and at the blackboard.

As usual Steve's attention had lagged. Suddenly he was returned to boot camp reality; Bud, sitting next to him, elbowed him in the ribs and whispered, "Hey, look who's coming!"

Steve looked up. Lieutenant Colonel Barton was striding along a graveled path that bordered the training area.

The recruits frequently saw Barton making tours of the battalion area. He made at least two a day, some early in the morning before chow, others late at night.

This time, though, there was something forceful about his bearing which suggested that his mission was more specific. He hurried along, swagger stick grasped in his left hand.

Several other platoons were occupying other bleachers in the area but the battalion commander passed these and kept coming toward 164. The special instructor and the drill instructors saw him but continued with the demonstration.

It was Dence, always eager to appear alert and officious, who called out, "Platoon, ten-chun!" when the battalion commander neared.

The recruits scrambled noisily to their feet, and stood at attention in the bleachers. The instructors came more naturally and smartly to that position by the blackboard.

Steve was high enough in the bleachers to see everything. Lieutenant Colonel Barton walked briskly up to the blackboard, glanced quickly over each instructor, turned and studied the platoon for a minute and then ordered, "At ease."

He spoke to the senior instructor, Swifteagle, and said, "Tell the platoon to be seated."

Swifteagle ordered, "Platoon 164, seats." In unison the recruits seated themselves and were still.

The officer took the throat microphone from the special instructor and slipped it around his neck. After clearing his throat and checking the amplifying system's volume the battalion commander faced the platoon and began.

"A few hours ago I received a report that a near fist fight took place this morning between two members of this platoon. The Marine Corps frowns on this method of settling differences, but we all know that they're bound to take place from time to time. I wouldn't be talking to you this afternoon if this had been just an ordinary fist fight. It wasn't."

Steve could see that Barton was angry, even more so than he had been during the interviews over the rifle. The veins and arteries of his neck were thick and swollen; he stood there with feet fairly wide apart, slapping the tip of his swagger stick into the palm of his hand to emphasize certain words.

"What took place this morning was a race fight. This I will not tolerate. Like a lot of other American institutions, the Marine Corps and the other armed services were slow, tremendously slow, to realize that the Lord didn't pass out brains, character or courage according to nationalities or the color of men's skins. That superman theory was Hitler's; our ideas of human equality come from bigger, better, healthier men—Jefferson and Lincoln, for example.

"In 1948 the color line was rubbed out in all the Armed Forces—Army, Navy, Air Force, Marine Corps. The system is working well, better than any of us hoped. As you know there are Negroes in just about every platoon on this base. And Mexicans. They make good marines, just as good as you are, whoever you are."

Here the battalion commander paused and sent his eye along every row in the bleachers. Steve could see that though his gaze was still intense, the heat of his indignation had burned itself out as he talked. When he resumed, his voice was milder.

"Now I know that Sergent Swifteagle and Corporal Bailey can handle any situation of this sort that presents itself. I came here in person because this subject is close to my heart. It's one of the things that I live and fight for.

"Your drill instructors will take suitable disciplinary action against the race-hater who started this morning's ugliness. I came here so that you would hear right from the horse's mouth that the Marine Corps is not out to separate Negroes from whites, Mexicans from Texans . . . merely men from boys!

"Any questions?" Barton asked, ending his brief talk in the standard Marine Corps way. "Then carry on."

As the battalion commander handed the mike back to the instructor, Swifteagle barked, "Platoon, ten-chun!" Lieutenant Colonel Barton returned the three men's salutes, flipped his swagger stick back under his left arm, adjusted his cap and set out across the sandy training field.

Nothing more was said that afternoon about Dence's act, and the training resumed. But that evening the Texan reported to the galley. No one knew for sure, but scuttlebutt had it that he was riding the range, and not on horseback as he had done in his Lone Star State. The ranges were the same ones the hoods of which Steve had cleaned. Dence also was relieved as leader of the 4th squad. Hernandez took that over. And in a talk to the squad, Sergeant Swifteagle made it plain that Manny had been assigned the responsibility and the authority for only one reason: he was the best man in the squad.

The march to the rifle range got underway right after morning chow Saturday. By 0645 the recruits and their sea bags were aboard trucks. The bags had been packed the night before when the huts had been cleaned and readied for use by some other platoon. Eight platoons joined 164 in the expedition to Camp Matthews.

The convoy pulled out the main gate and provided Steve and his fellow boots their first glimpse of the civilian world they had left behind a month ago. The trucks traveled first on a heavily traveled highway, then shunted off on a quiet road which led to a remote, arid canyon.

By 0700 the marchers had left the truck and set out on a rocky trail that traversed rugged mesas and cut through dust-dry arroyos. A captain commanded the expedition, assisted by three lieutenants. Each platoon had a Navy medical corpsman assigned to it. Two communications men with walkietalkies strapped to their backs were stationed at the point and at the tail of the column, which numbered more than 540 men.

Steve and the others quickly learned the first element of march discipline: Keep closed up. When the gap between individuals widened, the column stretched out. When the inevitable order, "Close it up, close it up" was passed, the men in the rear had to run hard to take up the column's slack.

Swifteagle reminded the platoon that this was the "accordion effect" and that though they were at the vanguard position during the first half of the march, they were to shift to the tail during the last half. They would learn there that "playing the accordion" wasn't any fun.

Shortly after 1000, the order to halt was passed down the column from its commander. Platoon leaders instructed their men to take off their packs and rest by the side of the trail. After a short repose there, during which they slipped on clean, dry socks which they had in their knapsacks, the recruits of Platoon 164 were called to assemble around Sergeant Swifteagle.

With his map of the area pinned to the earth by a small rock at each corner, the rangy Indian—who looked fresh and cool despite the fast pace and hot sun—traced the route of the march.

"We've come better than 9 miles in 3 hours," he reported. "Not bad for green troops. The last 4 miles are the steepest. Take it easy with water. Keep your packs tight; they'll chafe less that way." He told the platoon's corpsman to pass out two salt tablets to each man and make sure that they were swallowed.

In a few minutes the word was passed to resume march. Steve groaned and heaved himself to his feet. "This 10-minute break didn't seem to last 5," he complained to Manny. Bud

Ajamian, as platoon right guide, had to remain close to the
platoon leader, Sergeant Swifteagle.

As the column worked its way along up the steep grade
under a blazing sun, complaints about aching bones and blistered feet began to reach the medical corpsmen with increasing frequency. Several cases of heat prostration delayed the
march temporarily. Swifteagle repeated his earlier orders not
to take more than a few sips of water.

"Too much water is what's making these men sick," he
stated, pointing to the stricken recruits over whom the corpsmen were working.

At 1130, right on schedule, the column marched through
the main gate at Camp Matthews. When each platoon entered, its drill instructor ordered the recruits to open and
lock rifle bolts.

As his recruits pulled their rifle bolts back and locked
safeties, Swifteagle said, "That's the way your rifle will remain
at all times out here. The only time it won't be this way is
when you are on the firing line and the targets are up.

"Any man I find off the firing line with his bolt closed will
open it with his nose."

Steve shuddered at this prospect but understood that with
hundreds of boots, many of whom had never fired a rifle
before, firing live ammunition it took strict rules, strictly
adhered to, to prevent tragic accidents.

Steve and his fellow boots found the pile of Platoon 164
sea bags, which had been trucked out to Camp Matthews.
With the bags resting on their shoulders, the recruits made
their way under their drill instructor's direction to the tents
to which they'd been assigned. These were large, pyramidal
tents with wooden decking. They were equipped with a kerosene stove and six folding canvas cots.

Steve, Manny and Bud managed to get billeted in the same
tent. "This is going to be our home away from home for 4
weeks," Bud joked. "Let's try to live it up—if you can call
living in a tent and out of a sea bag living."

As soon as they'd eaten noon chow, they dug their blankets out of their sea bags, made their cots, policed the inside of their tent. Sergeant Swifteagle inspected, found things to his liking and marched the platoon to the mess hall to begin the week of mess duty which was going to precede their 3 weeks of training on the rifle range itself.

When the mess sergeant passed out assignments for the week, Steve got the "GI hut," so called because it was the place where the garbage was kept. The large galvanized barrels the garbage was stored in were called "GI cans."

The recruits whom they relieved explained to Steve and his three partners in the hut what the duty involved. When they heard a cook shouting, "GI, GI" they would head for the galley on the double, carrying an empty drum. This they would exchange for whatever receptacle was full and trot back with it to their less than fragrant shack. The various types of garbage had to be kept separate—eggshells, coffee grounds, grease, greens and peelings, general slop. All tin cans were smashed flat after their labels were removed. Paper and such trash was burned in a huge incinerator.

Next day in the chill darkness of 0300, Platoon 164's sentry awakened it. After washing and dressing, the recruits stumbled through the dark to the mess hall where cooks already had begun to prepare breakfast. At the rifle range, recruits had to be fed early—the firing began as soon as there was enough light to see the targets.

Steve found his own work hard and hateful. The other boys in the GI hut were big and willing. That afternoon Steve got a grim idea of what awaited him if he fell afoul of Marine Corps regulations again.

An evil-smelling garbage truck arrived, four Marine prisoners riding in the rear to do the dirty work. They wore distinctive brig garb—regular dungarees and shirt with white bands painted around the sleeves and pant legs and the circles of an ominous bull's-eye painted on the back.

The brig rats had the backbreaking job of hoisting the

garbage barrels to the platform of the truck. Two guards, both armed with riot guns, sat on the truck's cab, weapons at the ready, keeping careful watch.

Steve's work began early and lasted late. Not until the mess sergeant had inspected the galley after the evening meal and approved its condition could the mess-duty crew secure.

Back in their tent that night the three buddies compared notes. Bud Ajamian was in the commissary storeroom where he had to keep a record of food issued and received. "These guys know a wily Armenian merchant when they see one," Bud joked.

Manny had been assigned to the chow line, dishing out food.

"Situation normal," Steve scoffed. "Fletcher ends up with the dirty duty."

"Oh, it's just because the mess sergeant saw your big, broad shoulders and burly biceps, Buddy," Manny Hernandez laughed, expanding his own chest and flexing his own biceps in mock he-man fashion.

"Yeah?" Steve observed sarcastically. "All I know is I got the garbage detail and from about 0400 until dark I'm man-handling heavy GI cans. And I got 6 more days of it."

"Better not give any of those mess sergeants any static," Bud warned. "Some of those guys take themselves more seriously than D.I.'s. They'll run you up to the man so fast it'll make your head swim."

Steve, remembering the four forlorn prisoners riding the stinking swill truck, replied, "Don't worry about that, Bud, boy. Just don't expect to find me clutched with joy and all broken out with goose pimples when the band plays 'The Marines' Hymn.' I'll put into this outfit just enough to get by. When my 3-year enlistment's up, Brother, I've had it."

Bud Ajamian and Manuel Hernandez shook their heads. However, both would have confessed that it was a sad trick that assigned the most disagreeable mess-duty chore to the most disgruntled recruit in the platoon.

Chapter 12

DANGER'S FIERY FINGERS

THE days of mess duty dragged on. His wet, dirty, onerous job grew more burdensome to Steve. But the regular daily appearance of that garbage truck and its four crewmen served as a grim reminder. I've got to stay out of that brig, he told himself. This, he realized, was a negative attitude for Marine Recruit training, but it was the only emotion that drove him on.

The one consolation of mess duty came when the galley was secured in time and Sergeant Swifteagle marched the platoon to the movies. The drill instructor was taking advantage of the platoon's week of mess duty at the rifle range to requalify since all marines have to fire the range with the M-1 rifle and the .45 caliber pistol each year until they reach the age of 35. (Bailey had already done this and was away on a 30-day leave.)

Swifteagle took the recruits to the movies on both Monday and Wednesday night, the first movies they'd seen since joining the corps. It was an outdoor theater and the recruits sat in the sand, using their buckets for backrests, and wrapping up in their blankets to keep out the chill night air. Steve didn't dissent from his pals' agreement that this was fun.

So clean and complete was the break with the civilian world that Steve hadn't even read a newspaper since he left home. Newsboys circulated San Diego and Los Angeles newspapers at both mainside and the rifle range. The recruits, however, had little opportunity to buy them and even less to read them.

On Wednesday morning, while marching to mess duty, Steve and his companions smelled the unmistakable odor of smoke in the air. Steve asked a mess cook where the smoke was coming from.

"There's a big forest fire burning in a national forest about 40 miles from here," was the explanation.

Later that morning a newsboy passed the GI hut hawking newspapers and Steve bought an "Extra" edition of *The San Diego Union*. Banner headlines stretched across its front page, "Forest Inferno Perils Palomar Telescope" and in a four-column subhead, "Fire Rages Out of Control on Tinder-Dry Mountain Slopes. 500 Fire Fighters Flown In; All Available Marines from Camp Pendleton Being Rushed to Scene. Forest Ranger Chief Warns Only Shift in Wind Can Save World Famous Observatory with 200-Inch Telescope. 3,000 Acres of Cleveland National Forest Blackened."

The front page was also full of pictures showing scenes of the fire, its damage and how it was being fought. Before Steve could read any more of the details the cry, "GI, GI" sounded from the galley and he and a partner responded.

He never had a chance to complete his reading. When work for the day was completed, the fire had slipped from his tired mind.

By Thursday morning the acrid smoke had become much more noticeable. One of the cooks told Steve and his three partners in the GI hut that scuttlebutt had it that Major General Clendenning, commanding general of the San Diego Marine Base, had offered to supply "as many marines as needed" to help fight the blaze.

"Likely story," Steve scoffed when the sergeant had left the hut. "Boot camp is jail and jailbirds never get out until they do their time."

His irony was *not* well taken. Soon after breakfast Swift-eagle appeared in the mess hall area and collected his recruits. When the platoon had formed on the driveway behind the galley, Swifteagle broke the news. "The forest-fighting service has asked for 700 marines from the recruit depot to help battle a big fire in the Cleveland National Forest. General Clendenning has put Lieutenant Colonel Barton in charge of a detail of 10 platoons. Because you're on mess duty and won't miss training, this platoon has been selected. Others are from mainside. The convoy will be here in an hour. Go back to your tents, fill your light marching pack with clean socks, underpants, shirt, sweat shirt, towel and soap. Fill your canteens and also put bayonets on your cartridge belts. Make sure you have first-aid packets.

"Any questions? Move out. We haven't got any time to lose."

Platoon 164 double timed back to its tents where the recruits excitedly packed and prepared for the adventure.

When Sergeant Swifteagle had inspected each man, corrected the few deficiencies, the platoon double timed to the main gate of Camp Matthews. Only the sentry on duty and one relief were left "in the rear with the gear."

Little time had passed before the convoy churned down the highway. At the head of the column in a radio jeep sat Lieutenant Colonel Barton, a fat cigar jutting from his mouth. The driver halted abreast of Platoon 164, signaling the convoy to a stop. The battalion commander leaped out.

"Your people all ready, Geronimo?" he inquired of Swifteagle. Steve saw a grin spread over the Indian's face at the use of this nickname.

"Aye, aye, sir," he responded, snapping to attention and tossing Barton a smart salute.

The battalion commander was clad in dungarees, with the pant legs bloused into high-top boots. His cap's visor was thrust jauntily upward. Steve was amazed to see how sharp he looked even in field clothes. In fact all of the recruits envied Barton's salty appearance; his starched and faded dungarees had that salty look which the recruits hoped their own garb would acquire after suitable service—and laundering with strong bleach.

The battalion commander cast a quick look of inspection at Platoon 164. "Your men look ready. Take them on the double down to your trucks, the last three or four in the convoy. Tell the radio operator in the control jeep at the end to pass the word when you're all aboard."

"Aye, aye, sir," Swifteagle responded, again with a snappy salute. He gave the platoon "Left Face" and in an instant the recruits were trotting over the rough right-of-way bordering the shoulder of the road.

Steve counted 37 trucks. There were also 2 field ambulances, with large red and white crosses painted over the olive drab of their tops and sides. About 6 or 7 trucks were pulling 2-wheeled water trailers.

When the platoon reached the empty trucks, Swifteagle quickly organized the embarking. "The 1st squad get into first truck; 2nd squad, second truck; 3rd squad, third truck. First four men of 4th squad in first truck; second four in second truck; the rest in third."

Recruits jumped aboard. Men on the ground pushed those clambering up and men already aboard gave a helping hand, too. Before the dust could settle, everyone was in the trucks and the convoy rolled onward.

Fletcher, Ajamian and Hernandez were in the first of the platoon's trucks. So was Swifteagle. Following the drill instructor's directions, the recruits unslung their knapsacks and bedrolls, stacking them in the middle of the truck.

The vehicle was identical to the truck which had hauled Steve and Bud to the recruit depot from the Santa Fe Railroad Station. Cab and platform were canvas-covered.

"Just like one of those Conestoga wagons which brought the pioneers across the plains," Steve shouted to Bud over the roar of the motor and the noise of the canvas, which the wind was slapping about.

"You bet," Bud shouted back with a happy, excited grin. "We won't be shot at by murderous Sioux but I'll bet we see some adventure."

"Guess so," Steve agreed. Then he suddenly remembered that fighting fires was dangerous business. The memory of a scene he'd encountered in the High Sierras two summers ago awakened in his mind. He saw the blackened swath of a forest fire, dotted with the charred bodies of twelve men who had been trapped while trying to tame it.

After about an hour in which they passed through dry, rolling countryside, Steve felt the convoy reduce speed to pass through the streets of a small, attractive California town, Escondido. Then the grade became steeper. Instead of being cattle-grazing country, the hillsides were covered with orange, lemon and avocado groves. Steve and Bud and the others felt their ears popping as the convoy reached higher altitudes.

It was now past noon. The recruits, who had breakfasted at 0430 that morning, felt hunger pangs. Swifteagle spent most of the trip reading a pocketbook. Hearing the increasing mumble of discontent, the drill instructor looked up, examined his watch and announced, "We'll get there soon."

The Indian was right. In about 10 minutes the convoy slowed down, then ground to a halt. A wave of shouts rippled down the length of the convoy, passing the word order to disembark. The recruits slipped into their packs and dismounted.

The scene astounded Steve. Behind the highway lay an unfenced plain which apparently was the field headquarters of the fire fighters. There were three or four large tents, one of them a communications center with a tall radio antenna sticking out of its crown. Dozens of cars and jeeps were parked haphazardly around, their number being constantly augmented or diminished by vehicles which tore in and out of the dusty trail. Men hurrying around added to the sense of urgency the scene conveyed.

Steve and his fellows stretched their limbs and observed the activity. "Hey, Fellows," shouted Bud Ajamian, "look what's over there!" Pointing to the field on the other side of the road, he yelled excitedly, "Whirlybirds, eggbeaters!"

Steve squeezed between two trucks to get a better look. Eight helicopters were parked in an open field. Some crewmen were working on motors; others laboriously filled fuel tanks from 55-gallon drums of gasoline. A leather-jacketed group, pilots, studied a large map pinned to the side of a tent at one end of the improvised heliport. A forest ranger was briefing them, using a stick for a pointer.

"Looks as though we'll get some flight time," Steve remarked happily. "Ever take a helicopter hop, Manny?"

"Me?" countered Hernandez. "Why I haven't even been up in an elevator! That's why I joined the Marines . . . action, adventure, excitement, on land, on sea, in the air!"

"Also mess duty," Steve added drily. "Say, I wonder what happens next. Colonel Barton is making for the tents."

About this time Sergeant Swifteagle ordered Platoon 164 to assemble in the field on the headquarters side of the road. The other D.I.'s did likewise. Instead of having a long, straggly line, soon ten very alert groups of recruits awaited orders.

In a few minutes Lieutenant Colonel Barton returned with a forest ranger in a jeep, bumping over the rough field. Using the jeep's amplifying system, the special task force commander addressed his men.

"At ease, Marines," he began. "This is Chief Forest Ranger Glover," pointing to the green-uniformed man at the wheel. "He'll give us his estimate of the situation and brief us on how we fit into the operation."

The ranger arose, took the hand "mike" and nodded in Barton's direction. "Thanks, Colonel. It's good to have more marines. Now maybe we can get the situation in hand.

"This fire's a bad 'un," Glover declared with a worried shake of his head, "one of the ugliest and trickiest I've seen in 30 years in the Forest Ranger Service. We've stopped it on the western slopes of Mount Palomar but it's still out of control on the eastern approaches. Over there the terrain is split by a lot of deep draws; the fire's been jumping across them.

Crews fighting in these narrow valleys have to watch out or they'll be trapped.

"Over to the east between the fire and the observatory, there's a mesa. Good tableland. We're going to cut a wide fire trail across it. That's where you marines come in. We've got crews there now clearing a heliport. We'll fly you men in there as soon as it's ready. They'll radio when that's done; we expect word in an hour or so. Meantime, it would be a good idea to get some rest. When we fly you in, we're not going to pull you out until the fire's licked.

"Not only are some of the finest oak and pine in Southern California going up in smoke but if that fire reaches the Palomar Observatory up there, it will destroy a lot of buildings and the heat could crack that 200-inch telescope they have.

"We want to kill that fire," and here the forest ranger paused, ". . . but we don't want to lose any of you if we can help it. So be careful; obey orders; watch out for wind shifts."

Lieutenant Colonel Barton took over. He ordered each platoon leader to send a detail of men to the supply truck to pick up enough C-rations to last each man 3 days. When these reached Platoon 164, Swifteagle had the recruits pack away all but one lunch unit. That they ate on the spot. Then the D.I. ordered the men to flake out on the ground.

Steve was sleeping deeply when someone shook him. "We're moving out. They got the new heliport ready." Regaining consciousness, Steve heard the explosive roar of helicopter motors. He leaped to his feet; he saw the whirling rotors suck up clouds of dirt and leaves from the clearing.

Under Barton's control, platoons hurried across the road, one by one. The men of Platoon 164 came out near the head of the line and were loaded, one 15-man squad to a helicopter. There were no seats. The men stood up, but were not overly crowded. Steve took a position near the open hatch, which was secured by a wide safety belt.

The noisy motor revved up, the whirling blades spun

around faster and faster. Steve saw that the strange craft was pulling itself directly up into the air. It was a mysterious sensation, as though gravity had been partially relaxed and the helicopter was floating skyward. Soon all of the eight craft were airborne and scudding over the countryside like low-flying clouds.

After about 10 minutes of flight, none of it much more than 300 feet off the ground, the squadron swung around a massive bluff which had been screening a large part of the mountain.

"Hey, look!" exclaimed Manny, pointing up toward the mountain's crest. Steve peered in that direction. Two silver spheres, one larger than the other, protruded like giant basketballs from the thick pine forest which blanketed the mountain's top.

"Palomar Observatory!" Manny exclaimed. "I didn't know that they had *two* telescopes up there. Look how close the fire came on this side." He pointed to a charred area which seemed to be less than a half mile from the observatory. It was as if a blackened tide had swept it, engulfing a huge area before ebbing out to sea.

The helicopters began to climb rapidly; Steve felt himself being pushed down into his shoes. Along with this most palpable ascent, the crafts were also changing direction constantly, encircling the peak. Much of the land beneath them had felt the inferno's blast and lay in ashen desolation.

No one had yet been able to spot any active burning. Suddenly the marines could see great white clouds of smoke, billowing up about 3 miles distant. A brisk wind whipped the smoke low over the ground.

"It's burning straight toward Palomar!" Steve shouted.

"A rough show," someone commented.

Then the helicopter began to settle. A sharp-eyed recruit spotted a clearing in the forest, crawling with tiny figures. "We can't land *there*," Steve declared. "Not enough room."

But the heliport grew larger and the figures became recognizable as fire fighters, stripped to the waist.

Two helicopters at a time were able to settle down into the hastily cleared heliport. Marines scampered out. In a few minutes all eight had discharged their loads and were hurrying back for more.

Lieutenant Colonel Barton, who had come on the first trip, introduced himself to several red-eyed, soot-covered rangers working over a small radio transmitter-receiver. After inspecting a map with them, Barton returned to the leaders of the two platoons on hand. Shovels and axes were issued and the battalion commander struck out, compass in hand.

The recruits followed single file. At the beginning they passed groups of fire fighters, digging and chopping in the thick forest. Then these thinned out and soon were no longer encountered.

"Wild country," Steve observed. Despite the underbrush and the rugged footing, the marines made rapid time. After a long sweaty hike, the column reached the area assigned to it on the map. Using prominent terrain features—ridge lines, a large rock, dead trees—Lieutenant Colonel Barton assigned each platoon a segment of the firebreak to cut. Sergeant Swifteagle asked a few questions and then set out to distribute his platoon along what in combat would have been called the MLR (main line of resistance).

The inferno was not close enough to be heard but clouds of smoke could be seen boiling out of the mountainside about 2 miles to the east. Now and then bits of charred ash sifted down from the sky; pungent smoke hung like heavy fog in low spots of the forest.

All apprehension left Steve, replaced by a gripping excitement about the adventure. Only one thing irked him. Sergeant Swifteagle had ordered a muster every hour. He explained that this would permit him to pass on new orders, distribute salt tablets and check physical condition of the men.

"If we muster every hour," he continued, "we'll know pronto if anyone gets lost or hurt."

"What does he think he's doing, making us drop everything we're doing and report every hour?" Steve inquired disgustedly.

"Sounds like a wise idea to me," Bud answered, as they worked their way to their designated area.

"Sounds like typical Marine heckling of the troops to me," Steve retorted.

Except for a break for C-rations about 5 o'clock, the recruits worked until it was too dark to continue. They unfurled their blanket rolls and went to sleep on the ground, which was carpeted by century-old layers of leaves and pine needles.

Long before dawn Steve was awakened. Standing up he was startled to see the progress the fire had made while they slept. It had come much closer, so close that he could hear its angry crackling and see ugly sheets of flame. Vines and mistletoe carried the conflagration from treetop to treetop, some of which were so dry that they became flaming torches with explosive sounds and suddenness.

As soon as there was enough light, the recruits resumed their work—frantically chopping and digging the firebreak. The encroaching fire increased the sense of urgency for the marines; they chopped and dug frantically all day, stopping only for their hourly assemblies and eating. By late afternoon the inferno had approached so close to the firebreak that small pieces of charred wood, carried aloft as sparks, fell in a steady cascade on the fire fighters. The forest was thick with smoke; hurrying about were the soot-blackened recruits who looked like actors on a ghastly science-fiction movie set.

Three men turned up missing at Swifteagle's last muster of the day. This was not unusual. At practically every assembly someone would fail to answer "here," when the drill instructor called out his name; a hurried search along the line and loud shouts had never failed to locate the missing marine.

An 8-man search party was promptly dispatched to locate the missing marines; the rest of the platoon sat around on logs or on soft earth. Steve sat quietly but he did not rest comfortably.

Several facts bothered him. One was that it was now early evening; the approaching darkness would make it hard to see or be seen by the missing men. Three recruits was a large number of men to turn up absent. This, too, troubled Steve.

But worst of all, his pal, Bud Ajamian, was one of the missing trio.

In 15 or 20 minutes word was passed that the search party had found two of the missing men and was returning with them. They had been working in a remote area and had failed to hear the call to muster.

As the search party returned down the fire trail with its missing men, Steve Fletcher jumped up on a tree stump so he could see who was being brought in. If the diminutive figure of Bud Ajamian were in the file, he would be easily recognized.

Steve looked anxiously up and down the column slowly straggling down the freshly cut swath in the forest. Bud Ajamian was not there!

It was growing dusky. Since it was definite that one man, Ajamian, was still missing, Swifteagle lost no time. Assembling the platoon in a tight semicircle around him, the D.I. speedily outlined his plan.

"We will form a line of skirmishers and patrol up one side of the firebreak and down the other, the entire length the platoon is responsible for. No one can remember for sure where they saw Ajamian last so we'll have to cover all the area." The big Indian paused and looked the platoon over. "It's getting dark fast. Remember to stay no more than an arm's length away from the man on either side of you. Try to keep the line as straight as possible. I'll be about 30 feet ahead. Guide on me. Any questions?"

No one spoke. Then Swifteagle asked, "Where's the rope?" Someone threw him a coil of ¼-inch hemp rope. He slung it over a shoulder like a cavalryman's blanket roll.

With a few simple commands the D.I. had the sixty men in the platoon extended in a single long line. He took a position at the line's center and 10 paces ahead. After checking to see that everyone was set to go, Swifteagle waved the line into motion with a wide sweep of his arm.

Like teeth on a giant rake, the recruits of Platoon 164 began to comb through the forest. For the first trip along the firebreak, Swifteagle took the line on the side closer to the fire.

The human wave rolled on, slowly but relentlessly. Like the rest of the marines, Steve kept his eyes on the ground, looking up every now and then to check the position of the man on his left and on his right and to see whether he was gaining on or falling behind Swifteagle, who was acting as the rake's handle.

Fletcher sniffed the evening breeze, which had freshened and was rustling treetops and whipping smoke through the forest. The inferno's roar had been audible all day. Now for the first time Steve could hear angry snapping as twigs cracked in the flames and expanding sap, converted into steam by the heat, burst the bark.

Looking toward the fire, Steve could see its orange reflection in the underside of low-hanging clouds. There were even small, advanced outposts of flame scattered here and there amidst the heavy undergrowth below them in the distance.

After about half an hour of fruitless searching, the line of skirmishers approached one of the narrow valleys which creased the mountain's slopes. Remembering the forest ranger's warning, Swifteagle had had the firebreak cut along the edge of the canyon rather than projecting it straight across the deep but narrow ravine.

Stepping over boulders, freshly felled logs and through thickets, the phalanx followed the firebreak's course around the bending brink of the canyon.

There was still no sign of Bud Ajamian.

As it curved in conformity to the edge of the plateau, the fire trail also sloped sharply upward and the flat valley floor fell away. The side of the valley steepened until it became sheer wall.

Steve looked down into the canyon and saw that the innumerable small islands of fire had widened; in some places two or three had spread into one another as waves on a pond overrun each other. Suddenly an expanse of pampas grass caught fire and the flames rippled through its tufted tops with great speed and crackling. In a flash the fire rushed to the very foot of the bluff along the top of which the platoon patrolled.

"Pull in over there," Swifteagle warned the recruit walking along the verge of the plateau. "If you fell off, you'd know what a hot-foot felt like, for sure."

The twilight had deepened markedly and the flames below were beginning to cast stronger shadows. By now Steve felt almost positive that the only way little Bud was to be found that night was for *him* to make the discovery. If Bud were lying hurt somewhere, knocked out, they'd never locate him until morning.

In the gathering gloom, the line of skirmishers struggled on more slowly. Swifteagle was forced to halt the platoon frequently to straighten it out and tighten it up.

"There he is down there!" The excited shout from a recruit burst a brief hush which had settled over the tired, shuffling marchers.

For a moment the recruits stood still. When the import of what they had heard became clear, they rushed to the edge of the canyon and looked down.

Steve was not one of the first to reach the vantage point. By the time he was able to get there, a group of marines had lined up along the verge, looking and pointing down into the gorge.

Steve peered over. There, down at the bottom of an almost perpendicular wall, lay the unconscious figure of a marine. It was unmistakably Bud Ajamian. Steve looked closely and intently to see if there were any sign of consciousness, of life.

The figure remained motionless.

"We've got to go down and get him," Swifteagle announced brusquely. "There's no time to lose. If that high grass goes up, Ajamian'll be a goner."

As he talked, the drill instructor pointed to the thick patch of pampas grass in which Bud lay. It was isolated from any burning but only 50 feet away a clump of brush burnt, sending up an angry shower of sparks. As the platoon had seen many times during its search, it took only a single spark to ignite the tinder-dry grass and touch off a blaze which could swiftly consume the whole expanse of grass where Bud lay unconscious.

Another menace was a moving ridge of flame steadily eating its way up the valley floor, fanned by the ever-freshening evening breeze.

"Someone will have to go down and get him at the end of this rope," Swifteagle announced. "Who'll volunteer?"

Before Steve could rush over to the drill instructor, Manny Hernandez was there, helping Swifteagle untangle the coil of rope which he'd been carrying.

"Ajamian's my buddy since the first day of boot camp," Manny excitedly spouted. "I want to go down and bring him back."

By this time Steve had forced his way through the cluster of men surrounding the drill instructor. "Hernandez isn't strong enough to hold Ajamian on the carry up the cliff. I am. Besides, he's my buddy too, since before boot camp."

Steve elbowed Manny out of the way and placed himself directly in front of Swifteagle.

"Fletcher's right, Hernandez. We need someone we're sure is strong enough to hang onto Ajamian. He'll be dead weight. There's not going to be time for two trips."

"But I'm just as strong as Fletcher," Manny protested.

"No arguments," Swifteagle barked as he set to work tying an improvised bosun's chair for Steve to ride in. Moving quickly, the Indian chopped off a 2-foot length from the butt end of a sapling he found fresh-cut on the ground. He used this as a seat and looped the rope around both ends and then formed a yoke for Steve to fit himself into.

Swifteagle distributed members of three squads along the rope like a tug of war team. The 4th squad he directed at the canyon's lip to stand by for any emergency.

As the drill instructor tied Steve into the improvised bosun's chair, he passed on some final instructions. "Stay loose. If you clutch, chances are we'll never get your buddy out of there in time.

"When you're down there and have got hold of him real good, yank the rope hard three times. That'll be the signal for us to start pulling you back. Any questions?"

Steve thought a moment. "How's the best way for me to hold him?"

"Know the fireman's carry?" Swifteagle asked.

"Yes, sir," said Steve.

"Well, use that but be careful the rope doesn't knock him off your back. Try to keep it toward your face."

Like a sailor going over the side of a ship, Steve rolled slowly over the edge of the precipice and started down. He had not been lowered more than 10 feet before he became painfully aware of a shower of dirt and small rocks pelting him. He squinted upward and saw that the rope was cutting into the earth at the point it made its angular turn downward.

Swifteagle saw it too and halted the descent. While Steve waited, wondering what could be done, he looked down at Bud. The fire's progress was startling! As yet the large mass of dry, matted grass in which his friend lay, still unmoving, was untouched. But two separate patches of flame inched toward it.

Steve looked up to see what was being done. Swifteagle was slipping a thick log under the rope. Held in place near the lip of the canyon by four recruits, the timber provided a hard surface over which the rope soon began to slither smoothly.

Steve's breath came easier as his descent resumed.

For the first 20 feet, the wall of the canyon did not fall

perpendicularly but sloped slightly outward. As he was lowered, Steve could follow the trail made by his buddy's fall. Clumps of grass and small trees sprouting out of the gorge's side had been uprooted as Bud had struggled frantically to arrest his slide.

The last 30 feet was sheer drop and Steve spun from side to side as the recruits, knowing that there was no time to lose, payed out the rope more swiftly.

Steve landed with a jar which toppled him to the ground. He scrambled to his feet, fighting the taut rope, and rushed over to Bud, about 5 feet away. He knew that his first objective was to get Bud out of there, but he couldn't help putting his ear to the fallen boy's face to find out if he were still breathing.

He was! Steve not only heard breathing but also a low, almost inaudible moan.

There was slack in the rope by this time. As gingerly as possible, Steve grasped Bud's arms and pulled him up. When he had the injured boy over his shoulder he grasped him securely. After some struggling, he worked the unconscious recruit around so that he was draped over his right shoulder. Quickly then he grabbed Bud by his left elbow and encircled the thigh of Bud's left leg with his own left arm.

Testing the carry by bending his knees several times, Steve needed to shift Bud but slightly before having his weight nicely balanced and well-secured. He struck out for the foot of the cliff, staggering slightly over the rough terrain with his load.

For the first time he became clearly aware of how quickly the flames had closed in. The patch of pampas grass was ringed by fire. It seemed inconceivable that it hadn't already been touched off.

After taking advantage of his last chance to get fresh grips on Bud, he bent low and leaned forward so that his burden wouldn't slip off; then he gave the rope three decisive tugs.

Steve knew that the worst part of the climb would be the

first 30 feet. It was up sheer wall, most of it flat rock. Yet they could not dangle free for then they would slap against the face of the cliff; Bud might easily be knocked from his grasp.

The only thing Steve could do would be to keep his feet on the wall and "walk" up it as they were being pulled in. This position would also keep the rope from digging into the cliff where it started to slant inward. And Steve knew that if he could reach this point, he could manage the rest of the pull without danger.

His signal had been received. The slack rope lying about his feet began to disappear and he had to sidestep to avoid getting tangled in it. As it tightened and grew taut above him, he felt the sapling on which he sat start to bite into his thighs. The added weight of Bud made more difference than he had realized.

When Steve had been raised to his tiptoes, he pushed off, tucked up his legs and swung in against the cliff. After bouncing there gently once or twice, he'd been pulled high enough to stiffen his legs, find footing, and begin to take tiny steps up the wall.

Matching the rope's progress, Steve looked like some giant spider, slowly inching his way up a single strand of web.

His plan for scaling the difficult first 30 feet of the ascent was working well. He had good control. But when he had changed position at the foot of the cliff, Bud's weight shifted from Steve's back and shoulders to his arms. Already the burden seemed to be pulling his arms out of their sockets.

Slowly, evenly, the two marines were pulled out of the flaming valley. Although his feet slipped several times, Steve never lost his position. Bud grew heavier and heavier; Steve grimaced and hung onto him.

Finally they passed the point where the face of the cliff pitched inward. Footing became easier to get and keep; Bud's weight fell more on his back and shoulders once again; Steve breathed more easily.

Now the tugs of the crew manning the rope came quicker.

Steve looked up and saw Swifteagle fairly close, peering down at him. The drill instructor was shouting something but in his excitement Steve paid no attention. He was straining but happy—it felt as if it were the last 100 yards of a mile race. The worst was over; the hard work that remained would be eased by the exultation of having saved his best friend from death.

Suddenly he was at the top. First his head, then shoulders surmounted the bluff. He looked down the long line of recruits on the rope, still pulling in unison.

Hands reached out to grab Bud's body. When Steve felt this, he knew the job was done. He fell over and lay on the ground. Eager hands unslung him from the bosun's chair.

Swifteagle was improvising a stretcher for Bud out of saplings threaded through the sleeves of dungaree jackets. When he saw Steve sitting up, he said, "Good work. You need one of these stretchers?"

"No, sir, I can walk. But my shoulders and arms sure hurt."

"Well, we'll take you back with Ajamian to the heliport. The corpsman there will check you over."

After sending two men ahead to the heliport to give advance word of the emergency, Swifteagle organized three groups of litter bearers to carry Bud. Just as the recruits struck out, they heard a great crackling below in the ravine. Suddenly a great globe of flame and smoke billowed up out of the gorge. "There go those weeds," Swifteagle shouted above the roar. "Just like straw."

When he was sure there was no danger that the fire would spread out of the valley the drill instructor ordered the platoon to resume march. Except for the litter bearers the recruits walked in single file. Darkness had fallen but the night sky was fairly light. Silhouetted against it, the trees on either side of the firebreak served as guides.

Steve marched along, his mind racing with memories of the exploit. He was right behind the litter. Although Bud was still unconscious, his moans and increasingly active movements showed that he was very much alive. This and the thought of his role in the rescue filled Steve with a glow different from anything he had ever felt.

By steady marching the group reached the heliport in little more than an hour. The helicopter had already arrived. Bathed in the bright lights of a portable generating plant, it rested there like some giant, ungainly bird.

The Navy medical corpsman was there, too. He checked Bud's pulse and breathing and then had him transferred to a professional stretcher which he loaded into the 'copter.

"Take a look at this guy, too, will you, Doc?" Swifteagle asked the corpsman pointing to Steve. "He's the recruit we lowered down into the canyon. Had a rough haul coming up."

Steve took off his jacket and T-shirt so that the corpsman could examine the source of his pain. On both arms and around his chest, the rope of the sling had raised ugly, red welts.

"Sergeant, we better take him along, too. The doctors back at sick bay will have to look at him. He may have some cracked ribs."

So Steve walked over to the helicopter and climbed into its darkened compartment where the stretcher bearing Bud had already been lashed. The corpsman hopped in and in a few moments the helicopter was pulling itself up into the darkness.

It took only a short time for the helicopter to reach fire-fighting headquarters; there Steve was transferred to a stretcher and this was placed in the cavernous 4-place field ambulance.

The vehicle lumbered back toward the rifle range sick bay. Then sheer exhaustion seemed to combine with the monotonous hum of the tires, for despite his pain and the unyielding rack on which he lay, Steve soon was slumbering.

Chapter 13

ANOTHER BARTON DECISION

STEVE slumbered soundly until a sudden stop of the ambulance shook him into consciousness. He felt the vehicle start backward slowly. Red light filtering through the small rear window and directions shouted to the driver suggested that the journey was over.

As soon as the ambulance's rearward crawling ceased, its doors were pulled open. Steve, who had been placed feet-first into the vehicle, twisted his head around to see where they were.

White-uniformed figures rolling a stretcher up to the ambulance and a red sign, "Emergency," burning through the night gloom from over a double-door entry, revealed that they indeed had reached their destination. They were at the accident entrance of the rifle range sick bay.

"Take the guy in the top litter first," cried a voice. "He's the one who's hurt real bad." Steve identified the speaker as the corpsman who had flown in the helicopter and ridden down in the ambulance with them.

Four corpsmen extracted the wire litter on which Bud Ajamian lay and gently lowered it to the wheeled stretcher. Steve watched them roll this up to a ramp leading inside the sick bay. A doctor, stethoscope dangling from his neck, strode alongside.

"How's he doin', Lieutenant?" one of the attendants asked.

"Still unconscious but his pulse is strong," came the encouraging reply. That lifted a load of anxiety from Steve's mind. He twisted around and awaited his turn to be pulled out of the ambulance. It came swiftly. Sitting on the stretcher, four corpsmen came coasting down the ramp which ran out of the dispensary. They dismounted and soon deftly transferred Fletcher from ambulance to stretcher and rolled him up the ramp, his eyes blinking from the bright red light over the portal.

He was wheeled into a treatment room and eased from the stretcher to an examination table. A doctor soon swept into the room, flicking on a big-domed overhead light.

"How are you feeling?" he asked Steve as he washed his hands and arms at a sink.

"Okay, thanks, Doctor," Steve replied. "My back and ribs feel pretty good now, but the places where the skin was rubbed off on my arms sure hurt."

A couple of corpsmen began to work on Steve, easing him out of his dungaree coat and pants, removing his shoes and swabbing off his injuries.

The doctor started his examination. As he felt Steve's arms for fractures, he asked, "How did all this happen?"

As modestly as possible, Steve recounted the evening's adventure. The doctor went about his work quietly, asking questions only infrequently. After a while he interrupted, "No breaks. A couple of torn ligaments, but no breaks. That's good."

"How soon can I get out of here, Doctor?" Steve asked.

"Oh, it's too early to talk about *that*. It all depends on how you feel tomorrow and what the medical officer in charge thinks."

He wrapped two large bandages as broad as brassards around the biceps on each of Steve's arms and taped his back and chest. After injecting an antitetanus booster shot and a slight dose of morphine to deaden the pain and induce slumber, the doctor ordered the corpsman to take Steve to a private room at the end of the enlisted men's ward. This time he wasn't placed on a stretcher, but rode in a wheel chair instead. He felt almost good enough to walk.

The drug the doctor injected worked well. Steve felt himself being carried off to sleep almost as soon as the corpsman had doused the lights and left the room.

As Steve expected, the sick bay at the rifle range did not depart from the early awakenings with which hospitals everywhere typically begin the day. He was aroused soon after 6:00 by a corpsman bringing a tray of food into the room. He was hungry and thus did not object much to getting up prematurely.

Besides, he wanted to find out as soon as he could when he would be released. He wanted to get back to his platoon, wherever it was. And he wanted to find out about Bud.

Soon after 8 a.m. a doctor and a corpsman entered the room. "Well, how's the young hero this morning?" the doctor asked, a broad smile on his face.

"Fine, Doctor, fine. But how's my buddy, Private Ajamian?"

"He's coming along okay. Got a bad concussion and some broken bones. But he's going to pull through with no strain—thanks to you, I understand." Before Steve could think of a way to acknowledge this compliment, the doctor stuck a thermometer into his mouth and the corpsman began to unwrap the bandages.

When the doctor took the thermometer out, Steve spoke up. "When am I going to be released, Doctor?"

The doctor, whose gold oak leaves on his collars revealed him to be a lieutenant commander, thought a moment. "Let's see. This is Saturday. You'll have to be kept here for observation until at least Tuesday. You'll probably get out sometime Wednesday. Unless you have a reaction—run a high fever or something like that."

"Can I rejoin my platoon?"

The doctor shook his head. "I hardly think so. On the

range here, if you lose more than 2 straight days of training, you get held over and assigned to a platoon a week behind your old one in the training cycle. Regulations."

Steve's expression darkened, mirroring his flagging spirits. "But what if I get out of this place before my platoon comes back from the fire?"

"Not much chance of that," the doctor declared. "We can't release you before Wednesday. Have to keep you here that long for your cuts to heal. All marines are being secured from the fire today; that means your platoon will resume training Monday."

"The fire all out?" Steve asked in unbelief.

"Just about. The winds have died down, they had a little rain out there and then the firebreak you gyrenes cut helped finish it up. The rangers and the Indian fire fighters flown in from New Mexico are mopping up."

Before Steve could pursue his questioning, the doctor and the corpsman strode out into the hall. Soon Steve heard conversation filtering in from the adjacent sickroom.

For a brief time he tried to hear what was being said, but gradually his attention shifted to inner thoughts. The more he pondered over these, the more surprised and elated he became.

His initial emotion was relief, coupled with exultation over Bud Ajamian's safety. Steve had come to like the helpful, cheery, gung-ho little Armenian as much as any fellow he'd ever known. His death would have been a painful blow. But Bud had survived that drop down the gorge, his brush with fiery death, and was on the mend.

These thoughts did not, however, dominate Steve's reflections. Neither did his own role in the rescue, though naturally he was proud of this exploit—especially of the coolness and physical strength he remembered having displayed.

What, then, did occupy the center of his attention? To what subject did his racing thoughts return again and again? To his outfit, Platoon 164.

He wistfully mulled over his chances of rejoining his buddies and completing boot camp with them. Bud Ajamian, he realized, was out of 164 for good.

But there remained Manny Hernandez and Big Jawn Gillyard and a half dozen other fellows—most of them from his 4th squad—to whom he had grown attached. Steve knew that he would miss these guys and miss them badly.

As for Sergeant Swifteagle—there wasn't a D.I. on the entire base who could match him, who was as fair, as rugged, as sharp in appearance, as well versed in the hundreds of things a marine had to know to be a good drill instructor. Certainly no other D.I., Steve reflected happily, could call cadence and drill a platoon as smartly as the deep-voiced Indian.

Reliving the dramatic episodes of the previous afternoon, Steve felt a surge of pride over the way his outfit responded to the emergency, which, he remembered with a wince, had been uncovered by one of the musters he had so resented.

Steve recalled that when Bud's failure to respond to his name at roll call alerted Swifteagle to possible trouble, the drill instructor had jumped into action. Using the platoon organization, he was able with a few simple orders to start the search quickly.

The recruits responded smoothly. Following Swifteagle's cool-headed leadership, they combed the forest. What a few weeks before would have been a confused, milling throng was now a co-ordinated team, obeying voice and hand signals with sureness.

The search led to success. Sure, Steve admitted, Lady Luck had helped. Had not a sharp-eyed recruit glanced in just the proper place, Bud's figure might not have been discovered lying in the tall grass as darkness descended. But planning and teamwork had set up the stroke of good fortune.

It reminded Steve of one of his father's sayings, "I'm a lucky fellow and the harder I work, the luckier I get."

His recollections became more vivid as he went over the incidents of the rescue. If there had been a slip-up during the descent into the ravine or the long haul out, it could have cost Bud's life, maybe even his own.

But Platoon 164 did not fumble. Its members went about their various, hurriedly assigned tasks without a hitch.

Steve remembered a book about World War II that his father owned, *The Battle Is the Payoff*. It dawned on him that he had had a chance to see the Marine Corps system pay off outside of combat.

We worked together, Steve mused. Isn't that what Bud said gung ho really means?

At this point, a resolution firmed itself in Steve's mind: he would return to Platoon 164. He didn't know how he would manage it; certainly the doctor's prognosis ruled out such a possibility. All he knew was that he would do it—one way or another.

"If the Marine Corps really thinks that its famous esprit de corps first comes from loyalty to a guy's own squad and platoon," he said in an audible, almost defiant whisper, "they can find a way. All they have to do is cut a little red tape."

This thought carried him back to the welcoming address that Lieutenant Colonel Barton gave during the early days of training (it seemed months ago), when the battalion commander declared that unless the recruits came to believe that theirs was the best platoon on the base, the training had failed.

Steve realized that he regarded 164 as the best on the base; best D.I.'s, best recruits, best everything. Did this mean that the training was succeeding for him?

Before he had much of a chance to answer this question or examine his reactions to the experiences of the last day, a corpsman appeared, pushing a wheel chair, and Steve was soon spinning along in it to the X-ray room.

After almost an hour there during which a doctor and two technicians took roentgenograms of his chest, spine, back and shoulders, he was wheeled into a treatment room where fresh bandages were applied to his lacerations and bruises. To Steve's discomfort, he also got two more injections.

While in this treatment room, one of the corpsman told him that Bud Ajamian had been transferred to the big naval hospital in San Diego's Balboa Park.

By the time Steve got back in bed in his own room at the end of the ward, lunch was being served. He ate hungrily and, after eating, great drowsiness engulfed him. He rolled over and went soundly to sleep.

Steve did not know how long he had been napping when he gradually awoke and became aware that there was a tall figure standing at the foot of his bed, looking down at him.

"Afternoon. It's visiting hours and I thought I'd come by and see how you are progressing."

Steve looked up, squinting. His visitor was Lieutenant Colonel Barton.

"Good afternoon, sir," Steve blurted, trying to pull himself into a military posture.

The battalion commander circled the foot of the bed and came alongside. He put a hand on Steve's shoulder, saying, "Stay at ease, Fletcher. The *real* ease. How are you feeling now?"

"Fine, Colonel. They've got me strapped pretty tight with adhesive tape and it itches. But otherwise I feel no pain."

"Glad to hear it. Guess you had a close one out there yesterday. Anything I can do for you?"

"Not that I can think of, sir. These corpsmen here take pretty good care of me."

"Navy corpsmen always take good care of us marines, especially in combat," Barton declared with a serious look. "But isn't there anything you want. Razor? Toilet gear? Stationery?"

Steve pondered. There certainly *was* something the battalion commander could do. But the recruit wasn't sure whether it would be prudent to make the request. Suddenly he steeled himself and risked the rebuff.

"Colonel Barton, sir, yes I do have a request. Maybe it's

a big one that I shouldn't ask, but it means an awful lot to me."

"I hope it's not a request for special leave. Go ahead, shoot."

"I want to go back to my old outfit but the doctors say that I'll have to stay here until Wednesday or so."

A slight frown flickered across the battalion commander's face. "That might not be so easy. Let's see, your platoon begins its first week of actual training here at the range on Monday. As it stands now, you'll miss 2, probably 3 days of training."

He shook his head. "That's a long time. Most of the first week out here is spent 'snapping in'—learning how to hold the four positions you use when you fire, how to squeeze the trigger, and how to get the correct sight picture on small-scale targets. You won't fire a shot but snapping in is absolutely essential for actual firing. Even marines with 15 and 20 years of service try to get some snapping in work every year when they fire for requalification."

"I know, Colonel, but I've got some real buddies in that platoon. I'd hate to have to start with a new outfit," Steve protested, rising up on one elbow. "I feel I'm a part of 164."

"That's the best reason in the world for wanting to get back to it," Barton acknowledged emphatically. "Tell you what I'll do. I'll get in touch with the medical officer in charge. I'll try to have him give you a special examination Monday and release you that day if he can possibly see his way clear to do it. If you get out Monday you can rejoin your platoon with no strain."

"That's swell, sir," Steve enthused. "I really appreciate it."

At that point, Lieutenant Colonel Barton picked up his gloves and swagger stick from the bed and started for the door. "I'll have to go now, Fletcher. Good to see you. Before I leave I want to tell you that Sergeant Swifteagle sent in a letter of commendation to battalion headquarters about the way you handled yourself yesterday, rescuing Ajamian. That's fine. I'm glad to see you making the kind of record that I knew you could. It made my decision about you look good. That I liked too."

These words were spoken as the battalion commander backed out of the sickroom. He paused for a moment in the doorway to finish his sentence and then disappeared into the ward with a half-wave, half-salute.

The departing message stirred Steve. In his excitement over the officer's visit and the discussion about returning to his platoon, Steve had forgotten all about his exploit at the fire, to say nothing about the earlier court-martial and reprieve.

Lieutenant Colonel Barton couldn't have brought up the two subjects more effectively. By pairing them, the impact of his approving words was more than doubled.

Steve felt fine about the interview. Not merely because the C.O. congratulated him or because the way had been cleared for his return to Platoon 164, but also because it was good to be in an outfit with officers such as Barton who thought enough of their enlisted men, even recruits, to take time on a Saturday afternoon to visit them in sick bay.

The rest of the weekend passed uneventfully. Monday morning nothing developed, and by midafternoon, Steve had reluctantly concluded that the battalion commander had forgotten or been overruled on his promise. Just then a Navy three-striper, a full commander, came into his room with two junior doctors and a pair of corpsmen.

"Understand you want to go back to duty," the doctor announced.

"Yes, sir," was Steve's emphatic response.

The doctors checked the medical chart which hung on a clip-board at the foot of Steve's bed, and asked numerous questions. Then they examined him and had him walk up and down the room several times.

"You got shaken up out at the fire more than you realize— emotionally as well as physically," the doctor said. "We wanted to keep you here under observation for a few more days. But the bruises and lacerations are healing well, and your attitude is excellent."

He paused a moment, thinking. "Yes, I'll send you back to active duty this afternoon if you promise that you won't roughhouse. That could be bad for your back."

"I promise, Doctor," Steve replied, holding his right hand aloft like a Boy Scout pledging "scout's honor."

"Good." Turning to one of the other doctors, the commander said, "See to it that Fletcher is released as soon as possible. He has to get back to his platoon today."

With that, the entourage strolled out of the room.

Steve's spirits surged skyward.

Chapter 14

THE BIG PARADE'S BIG SURPRISES

MORE swiftly than Steve anticipated, the wheels of hospital administration began to spin. Within an hour after the commander's order, Steve had his release and, clad in his smoke-smelling dungarees, was trudging toward Platoon 164's tents.

He found his mates sitting around on their bunks, cleaning and oiling their rifles while waiting for the bugle call to sound evening chow. As he walked into his tent, Manny Hernandez jumped up and Steve had to step away gingerly from a backslapping reunion.

After this, Steve sought out Sergeant Swifteagle in the D.I.'s tent and gave him his sick bay release chit. The drill instructor then sent Steve hurrying off to the quartermaster's shed for a shooting jacket; this turned out to be a canvas coat with padded elbows and a pad around the right shoulder to cushion against the rifle's recoil.

Before 0700 the next morning Steve had his first taste of snapping in, and learned the rudiments of the technique by which the Marine Corps can transform a youth who has never fired a shot into a sharpshooter who can take aim from the 500-yard line and pepper a bull's-eye no bigger than a piepan.

Though his back bothered him, particularly when he contorted himself into the cramped sitting position for firing, Steve lost no training time. By the end of the week his back was so improved that the corpsmen at sick bay ripped off the yards of adhesive tape which bound him.

On Monday of the second week, the real fun began. The recruits took their M-1 rifles to the range armory where Marine gunsmiths checked over the weapons, particularly the important sights, and installed firing pins in the bolt so that the Garands could actually fire.

The platoon marched to one of Camp Matthews' four 50-target ranges. At the 200-yard line Steve met his coach. This fellow, a combat-proven marine—who had been a sniper in a reconnaissance company in combat—remained with Steve for the 2 weeks of instruction. During this period, the platoon shot in the morning, going over the same course and firing the same number of rounds that would be fired on the final Friday, *Record Day.*

It began at 200 yards, then moved back to 300, then back to 500—more than a quarter of a mile from the target butts. A total of 50 shots were fired, a bull's-eye counted five and a perfect score, "a possible," amounted to 250.

Steve did shoot well on Record Day, at both slow and rapid fire and from all four positions—sitting, standing (offhand), kneeling and prone. He dropped only 17 points from the possible total; his 233 score putting him into the most coveted class, "expert," whose minimum was 220 points.

He also shot expert with the .45 caliber revolver and did well on the familiarization firing of the Browning automatic rifle, the rocket-firing bazooka and the .30 and .50 caliber machine guns.

True the firing he did dirtied his M-1 rifle but all the work and drudgery made sense now. Steve realized his real test would come when the excitement and fun of the range were exchanged for the nerve-grinding routine, the unrelaxed pressure, the spit-and-polish of the main base.

Yet while he knew the final phase was going to be tough—with written tests and pencil work—Steve did not dread it. When he had been in the midst of that forest fire he had learned to understand the why of Marine Corps recruit training, that is to say, the why of the Marine Corps. Sure, there would still be inspections and close-order drill and other fussy things which used to irk him. But he sensed it was going to be different now.

Right after chow on the final Saturday morning, the recruits of Platoon 164 threw their sea bags aboard trucks and then jumped aboard themselves.

As the long convoy snaked through Camp Matthews' main gate, Steve felt more than a slight twinge of regret. The weeks out there had been fun, all except for the mess duty, of course. He had really learned how to shoot and how to handle and clean weapons properly.

Platoon 164 had 100 per cent qualification—every man had a Record Day score of 190 or more. Besides himself there were twelve other men, an unusually high number, who had shot expert. Billy Joe Dence had been one of these. But this didn't annoy Steve. It pleased him, in fact, because it pulled up the platoon's record and put it in a better position for the honor platoon pennant.

But these thoughts were not the main ones which occupied Steve during the ride down the Pacific Coast Highway, south to the main base.

What he did marvel at was the vast change which had taken place in all of them during the weeks at the range, especially in himself. He thought back to his reflections in sick bay the morning after he had been brought in from the fire.

He was conscious now, that it was at this point that the pieces of Marine Corps training fitted together for him and made a whole. His loyalty to the Marine Corps had not been forced. He did not come to think this way because he wanted to—it just came naturally, partly as a result of seeing it put to the test, partly as a result of the comradeship he felt toward his mates of 164.

If Steve experienced quiet elation during this ride, Dence, the usually talkative Texan, did not. In fact, he was downright unhappy.

The afternoon before they left, Sergeant Swifteagle had

watched Dence walk away from mail call and had seen him throw an envelope on the company street. The D.I. made him dig a deep hole in the hard adobe and throw the piece of trash in it. When Dence had it fully covered, Swifteagle had him dig it up again, read the address aloud to make sure that it actually had been mailed to him, and then rebury it. The pit was well over 6 feet deep and 3 feet wide. Dence's hands were blistered and he was whimpering about that on the windy ride back mainside.

Less than 48 hours after returning to the less eventful and much stricter life, which centered about classrooms and the parade ground rather than a rifle range, Steve was no longer troubled about his ability to stay on the beam. Even the threat of brig time failed to disturb him. He knew he would be able to succeed.

His experience proved something his father had often told him: a person's attitude toward something can shape his reaction to it; a healthy spirit can make a hard experience a rewarding one.

Steve's object was no longer merely to get through boot camp but to try to get as much out of it as he could. His only regret was that he had malingered during the first month. To make up for this, he was determined to be that outgoing marine that Red Mike O'Hara thought he could be.

But there were *some* issues still in doubt. Where would he be assigned after boot camp? Would his leave enable him to be home for Christmas?

Assignment to the 1st Marine Division would mean hard, tiring duty. But even this Steve no longer dreaded. He knew that by the time he got there he would be combat-ready, in good physical condition and able to give a good account of himself.

In this state of mind, the remaining weeks of boot camp raced by. In these final weeks the recruits of Platoon 164 concentrated on winning the honor platoon award. This was based on results of the three platoon inspections, its pencil work (grades of the recruits on written examinations), scores from rifle range qualification and the competitive drill held at the end of the ninth week of training.

Some weeks a battalion found that none of its graduating platoons came up to the required standards. When a platoon did win the award, it meant something. All eyes were on it as it marched along, its right guide carrying the honor platoon guidon, a small crimson and gold pennant, fluttering from a flagstaff. It was also carried in the final Friday afternoon parade when recruits wore their forest-green uniforms and low-cut brown shoes for the first time.

The day before the competition drill, Platoon 164 spent hours on the parade ground. Sergeant Swifteagle put the unit through all the marching and manual-of-arms commands. When he had exhausted his store, Corporal Bailey took over and tried other combinations. For competition drill the next day, Sergeant Swifteagle would draw twelve slips of paper out of Field Sergeant Major O'Hara's hat. With Red Mike and three other senior N.C.O.'s judging, Platoon 164 would react to the commands written on those slips as Sergeant Swifteagle called them out. Three other platoons of the 1st Recruit Training Battalion would participate.

On the eve of the drill Corporal Bailey gathered the recruits in one quonset hut and informed them that because of their 100 per cent qualification on the rifle range, Platoon 164 had a good chance to win the honor platoon award on the morrow.

"You'll have to be sharp," he warned. "There is going to be one other good platoon out there tomorrow. But there's one guy in this outfit—he knows who he is and you know who he is—who's goofing off, not keeping himself clean. Best way I know to straighten him out is to take him out tonight and have him trip over a locker box."

All the recruits knew that to "locker box" a man meant that all four squad leaders took joint action against the offender, who naturally was pulling down the entire platoon's rating. They all indeed knew about whom he was talking— Billy Joe Dence. He'd never really been much of a marine, but since his humiliation burying and reburying the letter, he had sulked and malingered. He had also developed a distaste for water and had zealously refrained from showering; so completely had he refrained that some of his neighbors in the hut began calling him "Billy Goat Dence."

Late that evening, the four squad leaders, aided by Steve and Manny, dragged Dence from his bunk and out the back door to the bathhouse. While four boots held him down, the two others scrubbed him vigorously with sand, soap and rough scrub brushes.

The "GI bath" not only cleaned Dence up for the competition drill, but also chastened his spirit. The next day, with hardly a flaw, Platoon 164 executed all the commands which Sergeant Swifteagle picked out of a hat at random. Shortly after lunch Lieutenant Zanutto sent word from the battalion operations and training office that Platoon 164 had been designated an honor platoon.

At simple ceremonies the first thing next morning, Lieutenant Colonel Barton presented the cherished guidon to Sergeant Swifteagle, who in turn passed it on to Manny Hernandez, currently acting as platoon right guide since Bud Ajamian had been hospitalized. In a brief talk, the battalion commander told the recruits that this was the fifth consecutive honor platoon which Sergeant Swifteagle had brought through boot camp.

Now the only big questions on everybody's mind were, "When do we get our orders and where will we go?"

On the last Wednesday all the recruits picked up their forest-green uniforms at the tailor shop, fitted and pressed with knife-edge creases. Their shoes had been previously issued and by this time had been "spit-shined" until they had a patent leather gloss.

During these last few exultant days the platoon reached its final stage of perfection. On a trip to the photo shop, it marched with such smartness and precision that several civilian cars stopped so their occupants could observe more closely. One of them was a big, black sedan bearing the two-star license of Major General Clendenning, the base commander.

Both Sergeant Swifteagle and Corporal Bailey relaxed ever so slightly during the last few days, letting down their mask of impersonality a trifle. This was particularly so when Bailey took Steve, Manny and a few others in the 4th squad on a special liberty to the naval hospital to see Bud Ajamian. It was a wonderful reunion, but Bud was moist-eyed with regret at not being able to outpost with his outfit. Not a word about his part in the rescue did Bud mention to Steve. But the latter could tell by Bud's glances at him how he felt.

On one of the very last mornings Sergeant Swifteagle showed that he would accept no deterioration of platoon discipline; feeling that the platoon had taken a little too much time in falling out, he dismissed it. When the recruits had filed back into their huts, he shouted, "Platoon 164, on the road!"

This time they were waiting for him, just inside the doors. They poured out and almost immediately froze to attention in ranks.

The senior drill instructor checked his watch and announced, "Eight seconds. Too slow. You could do it in 5 seconds your second week." He dismissed the platoon once more.

He repeated the process five times. Finally he was satisfied with the platoon's speed of assembly. The recruits were satisfied too. They knew that boot camp was still boot camp and they did not meander when either drill instructor shouted, "Platoon 164, on the road."

Friday noon, 24 hours before shipping out, the platoon's orders were passed out. Manny Hernandez was to remain right on the base for 8 weeks of radio and radar school; he was not on hand, however, to get his orders. He and a half dozen others were at headquarters, testifying at Corporal Gurdall's court-martial.

Steve was puzzled by the sheaf of orders Sergeant Swifteagle handed him.

> Pvt. Stephen Fletcher, USMC, will report 11 Jan—to commanding general, Camp Joseph H. Pendleton for four weeks duty with advanced infantry training regiment, upon completion of which you will report to commanding officer, Marine Barracks, 8th and Eye Street, Washington, D. C., for further transfer by government air, highest priority, to Moscow, Union of Soviet Socialist Republics, where you will report to the commanding officer, U. S. Marine Detachment, U. S. Embassy, for permanent duty.

Steve read this over several times, each time gaining greater comprehension, but still unable to understand, or believe, its full meaning.

"What kind of duty did you get, Steve?" Big Jawn Gillyard inquired.

"Read, will you and tell me if I'm off my rocker?" Steve replied, his voice ringing with excitement.

Big Jawn got the full import immediately. "Embassy duty in Moscow!" he shouted. "Dress blues and shiny shoes! You big bum, how did you manage to pull orders like these?"

"Beats me," responded Steve, shaking his head.

"Well," someone else broke in, "you complained because your big muscles and broad shoulders got you assigned to the GI hut at the rifle range. But now they call your build 'ceremonial stature,' and it gets you the best duty the Marine Corps has."

Manny Hernandez returned shortly, excited over the sentencing of Corporal Gurdall to 2 years at hard labor in a naval retraining command. But this was soon overshadowed by the news of Steve's orders and his own.

"It's like Bud and I tried to tell you, Fletch," Manny

shouted. "You can't beat the Marine Corps! You just can't beat the Marine Corps!"

Promptly at 1500 the customary Friday parade got underway. First the 50-piece band and drum and bugle corps played.

Then the adjutant ordered "Pass in review" and the 2,000-man column turned and swung past Major General Clendenning, his aide-de-camp, his general and special staffs.

As Platoon 164 paraded past the reviewing stand and cast "eyes right," Steve looked directly into the bleachers, filled with brightly clad civilians. His eyes caught sight of something that almost made him stumble.

There in the top row were his father, mother, and brother Roger!

He was sure that it was his family because all three were waving at him and because the boy had on a neck brace like Roger would certainly still be wearing.

Steve had received no inkling that his family would be down for the graduation parade. In a way he was glad they hadn't written that they were making the 500-mile trip. Then he would have known that they would be watching him and that awareness would have made him nervous.

But now that he knew it, the parade was almost over. He could hardly wait for the reunion and the chance to tell his family about his experiences and his exciting orders.

Sergeant Swifteagle dismissed the platoon at the end of the parade ground so recruits whose parents were on deck could see them.

Steve hurried through the dispersing crowd, hoping to catch his family before they started out to search for him. His heart seemed to jump a couple of beats when he caught sight of the three of them standing at the base of the towering flagpole near the bleachers. His father was pointing to various buildings.

Steve slowed to a more sedate pace and approached from the rear. Before his family knew it, he was standing in front, saluting his father by coming to "Present Arms" with his rifle.

His mother rushed up to him and threw her arms around him. "Steve," she cried, "you look wonderful. So tall and tan. But you've lost weight."

"No, I haven't, Mother. I actually put on 8 pounds. I weighed 176 this morning. I'm just harder. Here, feel those muscles!" He hugged her briefly.

"That was a pretty snappy salute you tossed me," his father declared with a laugh. "And, well, well; our marine is an expert rifleman." He stepped back and pointed to the silver medal that was on his son's chest.

Steve then turned to Roger, whom he treated more carefully because of the leather and steel neck brace which he was wearing, and which kept his face immobilized and his chin tilted upward slightly. "Hi, Rog," he said, shaking hands slowly. "Gee, it's great to see you looking so good."

"Well," his father interjected, "Marine boot camp certainly didn't do you any harm. Not a bit."

"I'll say it didn't," Steve agreed.

"When will you be able to get home?" his mother asked.

"I get 18 days leave starting tomorrow at 0700, Mom. I don't report to Pendleton until well after New Year's."

"Oh, you're being ordered to Pendleton," his father observed.

"Yes, Dad," his son replied, "but only for about a month. I go from there to Marine Barracks in D.C. for a course at the State Department."

Roger's face lit up. "You're going to be stationed in Washington, Steve?"

"No, when I complete the State Department course I'm going to be transferred for permanent duty to a guard detachment at a U. S. Embassy."

"Any idea which one?" his father pressed.

"Yes, Moscow."

"Russia?" Roger exclaimed incredulously.

"Not Idaho," Steve quipped.

"Well, this *is* something," Mr. Fletcher declared. "Expert rifleman and now choice diplomatic duty in Moscow. They must think well of you here, Steve."

"It wasn't that way for a while, Dad, but then I got with it."

Roger was fingering the material of Steve's blouse, observing his highly polished shoes. "Gee, Steve," he said slowly, "I always felt that you were the finest brother in the world. Now I know it."

Mrs. Fletcher was quiet but her eyes glistened with tears.

His father just nodded his head slightly and said, "Steve, your mother and I are both very, very proud of you."

Steve couldn't find words to reply. But he really didn't need any. When a young man gains his own footing and finds self-respect, those who know and love him don't have to be told.